THE QUIET BLOSSOM

A story about the Modern Wild West, the American Dream, and Marijuana

THE QUIET BLOSSOM

A Story about the Modern Wild West, the American Dream, and Marijuana

by
Michael A T Clark

DANCING MOON PRESS
NEWPORT, OREGON

The Quiet Blossom
copyright © Michael A T Clark, 2018
All rights reserved

This is a work of creative nonfiction. The events are portrayed to the best of the author's memory. While the events in this book are true, some names and identifying details have been changed to protect the privacy of the people involved.

Paperback ISBN: 978-1-945587-30-6
Ebook ISBN: 978-1-945587-24-5
Library of Congress Control Number: 2018959680

Clark, Michael A T
The Quiet Blossom
1. Marijuana; 2. Cannabis; 3. Green Rush; 4. Marijuana trimming culture;
5 Anthropology; 6. Social Movements; 7. American Sub-cultures;
8. Ethnography; 9. Memoir. I. TITLE

Original cover artwork: *Michael A T Clark*
Book editing, design & project production: *Carla Perry, Dancing Moon Press*
Cover design & cover production: *Sarah Gayle, Sarah Gayle Art*
Manufactured in the United States of America

DANCING MOON PRESS
P.O. Box 832, Newport, OR 97365
541-574-7708
www.dancingmoonpress.com
info@dancingmoonpress.com

FIRST EDITION

To The Sky

Thank you

Glenn Clark, Myles Stiffler, Cristin Waite, Tomas Zedinek, Paula Verez, Rafaela Alves, Chris Bisset, Alison Clement, Cole Robinson, Edward van Aelstyn, Mafalda Fernandez, Mike Clark, Wren Clark, Carla Perry

Contents

Book One: A Living Fantasy (Fall 2008)

Part 1

1

The cars passed in a blur, heedless of our hopeful thumbs. But we didn't care; our optimism was endless. It would keep our thumbs held high all that day and into the next if need be. We were standing by the road waiting for a vessel, one that would carry us towards our dream, a dream into which we were already wading and into which we were prepared to dive and let the currents carry us to a new existence. All we had to do was let go and go.

We were costumed in our worst garments and bearing a few artifacts that mostly served to show how ill-prepared we were: almost no money, too few clothes, threadbare jackets, a flashlight low on batteries, and giant smiles that made up for it all. Where we were going, there was no need for concern; all one needed was confidence and intention.

That was our take on it at least.

"Someone stopped!" Adrienne called to me.

I had spaced out and was staring at the sheep across the road, my thumb balanced in the air. I turned toward the voice of my companion. Some old tin box of a sedan was on the shoulder of the road with its blinker on. I shook vague thoughts from my head, hoisted my pack, and ran after Adrienne who was already conversing at the passenger-side window.

"He's going as far as the coast, Ben," she said as I trotted up.

"Works for me!" I replied, putting on a grin. I felt the excitement of the unknown lapping at my feet as I placed them on the floorboard of the car. A first ride is like starting a new book— the first chapter in an adventure that starts the moment you leave the familiar behind.

The driver pulled onto the road and the sheep fields and trees outside the window began to slip into the past. I turned my face to the road and looked ahead towards the hills and bends that obscured my view of what was to come.

I didn't know it then, but I was about to join a social movement, a small but significant cultural revolution that was, and still is, shaping the minds and ideals of American society. A movement that started within a small, isolated community and has since rippled out to leave its mark on my generation and the generations to come. I was so caught up in my short-term goals during that brief term, so caught up in self-confidence and manifesting my dreams, that I failed to see the greater significance until much later. At the time, culture, a changing society, and other significant undercurrents were far from my thoughts. What I was looking for, dressed in my worst clothing and thumbing cars, was money.

After names and thank-yous, and the first awkward pause, our driver asked, "What were you kids doing in Eugene?"

Adrienne was quick and cheerful with her reply. "Oh, we live there."

He nodded, "Mm-hmm, and why did you say you were going to California?"

I exchanged looks with my partner. The driver wasn't threatening, that was for sure, resting his elbows on his belly and rubbing his grey stubbled chin against his shoulder periodically as he plodded around the curves comfortably below the speed limit.

"Just going to visit some friends!" Adrienne told him with a winning smile.

The man nodded and we puttered through Veneta and up into the grey-green gloom of the coast range.

"And you? What were you up to in Eugene?" I finally asked, trying for a polite tone rather than a curious one.

Our driver gave me a wry look in the rearview mirror then allowed an apparently characteristic pause that seemed part of his sentence structure. "... Oh, I had to deliver some weed to a friend. Just a day trip."

I looked at Adrienne, who looked at me. The trumpets of victory were sounding. She fixed me with her gaze of *communication*, which we both felt could express everything necessary between us, and then tried for her own relaxed pause before destroying it with an over-eager voice and blurting our true intentions to the stranger.

"Well... actually, we are going to California to work on a pot farm!"

The driver nodded calmly. "Yeap, that's what I figured."

Maybe in later days I would have been bothered by his certainty and judgment of our appearance, and his assumption that we weren't letting on the truth, but in my naivety, it just seemed too remarkable to inspire annoyance. I laughed with pleasure at the clear awe of the situation, "That's kind of crazy, that our first ride is in the same line of business."

He lifted his chin in the suggestion of an impressed chuckle. "I guess so," he said, leaving unspoken the comment, *Well, it's not exactly rare to find an Oregonian who has some relationship or other with marijuana.* "Anyway, whereabouts is the farm you kids are headed to?"

Another look passed between the two of us. "Well, we don't actually have anything lined up. We just heard there was a lot of work in Northern California and that it was easy to find if you were in the area."

Our driver looked amused. "Well, I'm sure you'll find something." He labored at getting to something in his pocket and eventually produced a medicine bottle. He unscrewed the cap and pulled out a dense little bud, a bit brown and brittle, but offering up the familiar funk of weed. "Here ya go, a little something of mine for good luck!"

And that was that.

After parting with our driver, everything seemed so aligned with our goals that by the time Angelo picked us up in front of the state penitentiary outside Crescent City, we were pretty certain we were on the path of our destiny.

2

In reality, we knew almost nothing about working on marijuana farms in California. What Adrienne had admitted to our driver was all we had to admit. Eugene, Oregon, was not offering us all that we had hoped for in early October. We were living in a damp and mildewed house with at least eight other friends (depending on the day). I had inconsistent work in a musty warehouse building sets for a theatre company that was going under. And Adrienne had a couple of bartending shifts each week. Once the rain gets going in the fall, the few clear days are hard-pressed to divert your attention from the looming winter months. But California was the mythical land of eternal sunshine and, according to the shadow of a rumor going around, they were desperate for hands to process the endless fields of cannabis that grew to the size of small oak trees under the everlasting auspices of the sun.

I had been inquiring for several weeks about the particulars, but nobody in my circles seemed to know the specifics. Just that *it was happening there*, and *it could be done!* Otherwise, the apparent industry of our neighbors to the south was shrouded in mystery.

Finally, I ran into an old acquaintance who said he had done it, although he seemed a bit too casual about the scenario for how great it sounded.

"Sure man, you just go down there and hang out, and then someone comes around and says they need twenty people, and you hop into their rig and they take you out to their farm and you trim buds for a couple weeks, and then go to the next farm. You can make ten grand in a couple of months. You just camp out and they feed you and everything. Super chronic food, too!"

I didn't really need to hear anymore after he mentioned ten thousand dollars. I had to fight my feet to keep them from walking south that very moment. What the hell had I been missing out on? How had they kept this a secret? Well, I was getting in before the secret was out! No more questions needed asking!

I brought up the project with my household and expected them all to jump onboard, but to my surprise, everyone one of them shied from the adventure and I sensed undercurrents of apprehension.

"Ok, you guys don't know what you're giving up! It's a goldfield down there. Enjoy your unemployment in the rain."

Adrienne had joined my side and we regarded the others with hurt egos parading as supercilious condescension. I was thrilled to have Adrienne in on the quest, truly none would be better, but her one shortcoming was that, like me, she owned no car, whereas the others did.

"Really? None of you guys are coming?"

Peter finally spoke for them. "Honestly, it sounds super shady. I hear about it all the time, but I don't *actually* hear anything about it. Who is going to pick you up on the side of the road and take you to their house to trim weed?"

But the rumors and the mythos had gotten under my skin and it seemed that the harder it was to track down information, the more intriguing it was. Besides, at that time I didn't believe in my ability to fail.

And so there I was with Adrienne, hitching south, roaring down the coast in car after car, and everything seemed to resonate with the enigmatic air of marijuana. The driver of every second car from Eugene to Bandon admitted to some involvement with the plant of unparalleled abundance.

"Ohh, dash it all!" said the frumpy lady who picked us up in Yachats. "My husband and I grow a little in the back shed, just for a little extra cash on the side. Never hurt anyone."

The Holy Roller gave us a lift in his windowless van, spoke to us of Jesus, and then offered us a joint.

"Nnehh!" groaned another chunky woodland fellow as though he were succumbing to a heavy round of interrogation. He pulled out of the gas station onto the soggy highway in Coos Bay and we trundled south. "To be honest, I'm growin' a bit of weed myself."

Onward our journey progressed.

We were on the trail. As we camped that night on the beach and watched the full moon set on the silver Pacific, I allowed a benevolent sneer for my foolish friends hunkered under a moldy roof.

3

One would think that my naivety would come back and slap me in the face, teach me a lesson about overconfidence, but it never did. Old Tom was our last ride the next day, and he carried us across the state line into California. Adrienne and I had become good at exchanging meaningful glances and, with minimal preamble, confessing our intent to most of our drivers. After all, you had to put it out there if you wanted to find it, my partner opined.

"Ho-hoo!" said Old Tom. "It's the tune of the times! I've grown my fair share of the stuff, but I just lose all the profits at the casino! Anymore, I take one dime over the state line everyday to the Lucky 7. If I win in the machines, I keep playing. As soon as I lose it, I go home. Wife won't let me play with more! But I know life is just a gamble in the end." He beamed at us. "Well, you kids are going to the land of green and gold! Or so I was told. I hear it's a magical place down there. How about I wish you luck, and I'll bet I'm gonna turn this dime into a hundred bucks today!"

I told him I thought it was his day.

That night, Adrienne saw a mermaid playing in the moonlit waves. We agreed that was a good omen. We ventured out into the soft sands of the deserted beach to marvel at the California moon. Something indeed felt different—my fantasies ran away into the night and I resolved that I had stumbled into a children's book, a fantasy. I tasted magic in the air. It was as if we had crossed the invisible boundary into a world where anything was possible. It didn't matter if it was my imagination or not, because in the end, I had left what I did not like: a social setting where I felt trapped by outdated ideas. I had taken a leap into the unknown and I felt empowered. If I didn't find anything, then I could go back with an adventure to talk about. And if I did find something? Then it meant there was a hidden world of possibilities of which I'd been previously unaware right around the corner; a world where I felt certain things worked differently.

4

The Subaru wagon rolled up slowly and the passenger window dropped. Eyes scanned us from behind aviators. "All my best instincts tell me I shouldn't pick up hitchhikers by the entrance to a prison, but you guys look more like victims than perpetrators."

We blew through Crescent City and passed under the indomitable watch of the redwoods as we bobbed along to the Grateful Dead.

"What in the world were you guys doing by the state pen?" Angelo asked. I could tell he was working on the story he was going to tell his friends when he made it back to Seattle.

I shrugged, "Our last driver had business there. He didn't say why, and I didn't ask."

Angelo missed most of what I said because Jerry Garcia had kicked into a solo on "Not Fade Away," and he lost himself in the music, his hair hanging over his face, rocking gently to the guitar's plaintive call. I watched the road to ensure he stayed on course through the duration of his reverie. After an emotional sigh, he swept his hair behind his ears and resumed his attentive role at the wheel squinting down the road through those dark lenses. "I was at that show. I wasn't even a year old. My third Dead show."

We had told Angelo straight away what we were after in California. His bearded physiognomy and throwback jean jacket, along with the variety of Grateful Dead swag, had instantly eliminated all red flags. He took our news as though it were the most natural thing in the world, just as most of the other people we'd encountered had seemed to.

"So you don't have a place to go?" he asked, "Because we are getting into that zone pretty soon, and I gotta know where to drop you off." He understood our uncertainty in the pause that followed. "Ok, ok," he said. "I can drop you off in Arcata. There's a big scene there, and I won't be leaving you out in the woods somewhere, or by another prison... You guys really don't know anyone? No place to stay if something goes wrong?"

Angelo must have been in his early thirties, but after an hour in his car, he seemed to have developed a paternal sentiment. I could see why. I wasn't so blinded by my enthusiasm for the journey that I was unaware we radiated childlike helplessness and trust. We were traveling with open minds and ready smiles. That was something I knew we could be proud of and, despite our tattered garb, we made a point of maintaining appropriate hygiene, something that goes a long way when hitchhiking.

As we reached Arcata, Angelo appeared to have concluded some inner debate. "You know what, let's go on down to Eureka and stop for a beer at Lost Coast Brewery. I like to stop there when I'm down this way, and I could call a friend and see if he can do something for you."

We didn't want to presume too much, so we humbly acquiesced and told him any connection was appreciated. Secretly, my imagination was throwing a party. This sounded like a potential gig and everything felt as if it was working as it should.

"I was raised in the parking lots of concert venues, and the whole community took care of the kids," Angelo explained. "You guys seem honest and nice."

Adrienne and I had a quick staff meeting while Angelo wandered off to make his call. Our meeting was succinct.

"Do we need a contingency plan?" I asked quietly.

Adrienne shook her head "No way, we are in. I can feel it!"

Moments later, Angelo returned with a scowl on his face and my heart sank. So much for *feeling it.*

"Couldn't get a hold of anyone," he said. We watched him undertake another internal debate and my mind started to think about where we could pitch a tent.

"But I gotta come clean with you guys... I'm actually heading to my friend's place outside of Garberville right now to do a little trimming. And I think I'm just gonna take you along. I'm sure they could use the help."

Adrienne burst into a fit of giggles.

Wending our way south, the landscape glowed with increasingly golden light. The sun no doubt played its role, but I was almost convinced that the flaxen grass hills were giving off their own rich illumination. It spilled onto the pavement before us and stained it—our very own yellow brick road.

5

Garberville was lethargic in the late afternoon sun. Adrienne and I spent most of our Oregon food stamp money at the health food grocery buying dried fruit and nuts, and hoping that the rumors of on-site meals were a reality. While Angelo went about his provisioning, we sat in a small plaza pondering our incredible fortune and watching the denizens of the Northern California habitat. An ancient human with a mossy beard and a Baja hoodie was spinning slow circles beneath a large tree on the far side of the plaza, starring up into the boughs with dauntless attention. A woman in earth-hued yoga gear, and another with waist-length dreadlocks and a bone hoop through her septum, were conveying seemingly endless bags of groceries from the store to a massive diesel truck. Here and there, rugged men in slightly over-ornamented working garb moved purposefully about their business.

There was even a little pile of youth on the curb down towards the main street. They looked more appropriate to the milieu than Adrienne and I. Our uniform of tattered clothing consisted of a pair of old jeans and a t-shirt with holes. The party down the street looked like a traveling circus that might miraculously vanish amidst the lingering cloud of smoke. I was secretly pleased that we had fortuned onto Angelo. I didn't think we could compete with the circus people if we were standing by the road waiting for an employer. And, to my amazement, and fitting with everything I had come to believe about that miraculous wilderness, a truck pulled up and hailed the circus. A gaunt boy hoisted himself and loped to the vehicle holding up his capacious patchwork pants with one hand. A moment later, he signaled to his cohorts and they all piled into the bed of the truck that disappeared down the road.

"Holy shit! Did you see that?" I asked Adrienne.

"Yeah… what is this place?"

6

We followed the dizzying road east into the hills, flashing from shadow to sunspot along the winding traces. Up and up we went, back and further back into the hills, ever deeper and more removed from civilization. And then, at the glorious moment of the sun's final bow after its day's performance, we crested a rise and saw the last farewell of the light hovering above King Peak in the west. And it was breathtaking.

"This is it," said Angelo, hopping out of the rig and fiddling with the number code on the gate lock. I breathed in the fragrance of the Manzanita and dry grass. The brilliance of the last light made my vision swim and I couldn't focus on anything in particular so I just sat back and felt grateful. Angelo climbed back into the car and we rumbled down the gravel road towards the receding light. Adrienne finally asked a question both of us had been far too embarrassed to pose.

"So what, exactly, is trimming?"

Book One

Part 2

1

I was so enchanted by the luck that we had worn like a cape into the California badlands that I half-expected to come around the bend and find a castle guarded by wise and solemn dragons that would bow to us and usher us down a velvet carpet. My castle turned out to be a thirty-foot canvas yurt and a wooden shed. However, I was no less pleased.

We stood awkwardly in the dusk, unsure of where to place our attention while Angelo disappeared to speak on our behalf. A couple of girls were sitting in a haphazard ring of canvas camping chairs pawing through plastic trays piled with plant matter, and chattering. A number of the chairs were empty. Several yards off, where the hill sloped down steeply towards the western pink, other ladies were silhouetted in iconic yoga poses, standing one-legged like storks or sitting straight-backed with their palms pressed together high over their heads. No one paid us much attention, so I just absorbed the view of the King Range and inspected the lay of the land.

From where we had entered the property at the top of the ridgeline, we had to descend a steep hill through the long grasses for a half-mile before arriving at the development, a graveled terrace on the mountainside. The terrace had enough room for only the shed, a small aluminum pole tent, and the yurt. The yurt was situated on a concrete slab that appeared to have been poured for this purpose. It was staged on the very edge of the terrace where the land fell away—a regal position, not so unlike a castle. Behind the yurt and shed, a ravine was gouged straight down the slope of the hill. Advantageous oaks had crowded in and were old enough to peak over the top of the structures onto the gravel area where we had parked. This open area in front of the yurt seemed to be the center of activity. It was the driveway, but served as a courtyard for work and gathering as well. The estate was rudimentary, but very neat. There were even a couple of potted plants on both sides of the yurt's entrance.

The workday was ending and darkness was silently settling onto the hills. The girls seated in the circle began to abandon their stations. I had the momentary thought that we might be turned away. These strangers had no commitment to us, and they seemed well staffed with attractive young women.

"You guys came with Angelo?" A clean-shaven, clean-cut man with fleshy eyelids and a boyish face walked around the corner of the shed and then towards us with a welcoming smile. He reached us with his hand out and we shook. "I'm Isaac. Welcome. Are you guys hungry? We are about to have dinner."

We certainly were!

Angelo appeared and gave us a reassuring smile. "They were a little annoyed that I didn't call before bringing strangers, but they said they should be able to put you to work. No stress!" he said quietly.

Another man, this one with a crew cut, emerged from the shed and approached. We shook hands and he regarded us coolly. "Derek. Nice to meet you. Do you guys have any experience trimming?"

We shook our heads no.

"Ok, well, we can try things out for a few days and see how it goes. We will provide meals while you're here. You have camping gear?"

"We have a tent," I said.

He gave a curt nod. "All right. You can set it up anywhere down the hill over there. Come on into the yurt to meet the crew. You guys are welcome."

This last *welcome* seemed to come from a place of good upbringing and instilled values of hospitality rather than from genuine enthusiasm, but no matter, we would prove ourselves. We thanked him profusely. As I walked towards the lighted doorway, I recalled that only that morning I had been just inside the California border with no clue of where to begin the search for work. And now, as though foretold, we were in! It was just Day Three, and all the mysterious rumors and unbelievable promises of abundance had come true.

2

Stepping into the yurt strained my sense of reality again. The rugged wilderness and the simple homestead tucked away on a remote mountainside gave way to white carpets, plush sofas, and a large-screen television. The woodstove in the center was enjoying its own food and cackling happily. Isaac and one of the girls were standing in a thoroughly modern kitchen, putting the last touches on a meal that I guessed would make me cackle with happiness too.

There were several partitions on the far side, and through a parted curtain, I could see an enormous bed with a downy comforter and bursting pillows.

"There are beers and coconut water in the fridge," said Isaac. "Help yourself to whatever!"

We introduced ourselves to the girls—five total. They all smiled and exchanged greetings and asked the perfunctory questions, but we didn't go beyond that because dinner was announced. I was relieved and I could tell that Adrienne was as well. I felt drained.

We sat on the floor in the living space and ate. Everyone had his own approach to the supper routine. Angelo, who was apparently a long-time friend of Isaac, descended on his hearty pile of food, eating liberally and teasing Isaac about his inability to cook Italian cuisine properly. Isaac sat with his girlfriend, Mandy, at a small table they'd set with glasses and other accoutrements. He replied to Angelo that the arrival of an Italian meant they had a new cook. A few of the girls meditated for some time before touching their plates. Derek came in from outside, collected his meal, and disappeared again. It felt simultaneously familial, and industrial. Workers taking their meal after a long day, seated together in a decadent abode, comfortable, carefree and at ease, shutting out the flinty realities of the world just outside the door.

I volunteered to do the dishes, which gave me the relief of avoiding further conversation, and then Adrienne and I excused ourselves with much show of gratitude to erect our tent. The black emptiness that greeted us outside the yurt was startling. An hour or two within the soft ease of the yurt and I had already forgotten where I was. The warmth and comfort immediately vanished and the yellow light peering from the windows was swallowed before it could unveil any secrets. The soft hum of the generator, which might have been an annoyance, was a necessary reminder that we weren't hopelessly lost and forlorn in a hostile wilderness. But even that disappeared as we dropped down the hill.

The moon was not yet up and the stars crowded for space in the sable expanse. The temperature had fallen and the cold began to work itself under my layers. Unfamiliar sounds indicated the presence of others, as did the eyes that glinted when my flashlight beam swept the surroundings. We located an area reminiscent of flat, and battled with our tent in the darkness. My feeble flashlight was more of a hindrance than aid. As we cursed the poles into their appropriate formation, we couldn't help but notice the ring of eyes that had formed around us and was slowly drawing closer.

3

Adrienne and I lay in our sleeping bags shivering. Neither of us had a pad or pillow. The slope turned out to be more substantial than estimated and sleeping anywhere but at the bottom corner of the tent required active climbing. Fortunately, there were enough rocks beneath us that I figured I could wedge my feet against them and perform a sort of standing sleep.

At some point that first night, I woke to the sounds of the coyotes as they cried at the moon. The tent glowed and I crawled out into the biting air. The land was illuminated in soft silver; the moon was rising over the hill behind us. There was nothing stirring but the song of the dogs and the cold light from the heavens. I felt alone in the world and that was ok. I was inspired to cast off my clothes and join the coyotes in their lament, but it was rather cold, so I thought better of it and went back to my tepid nest among the rocks.

It became a ritual to climb out of my tent in the hour when that great nightlight turned on and listen to the music. In my memory, there was a full moon every night and the coyotes performed in four-part harmonies.

4

A wooden platform sat some distance from the congregation of buildings and we had walked by it in the night without noticing. It was a simple flat deck designed to not detract attention from the view for which it had been built. Atop it, a man was sitting on his haunches, hooded, and wrapped in a cloak. Based on his garments, I might have thought he was one of Robin Hood's Merry Men. He watched us from the corners of his eyes as we came up the hill.

The sun had not broken free from the hill and my breath exploded in clouds before me. I was cold, but I knew I was watched and I thought it important to be social. Besides, the King and Queen stood in the western distance bathing in the morning sun that had already reached them, vainly asking to be admired.

I sat next to the man on the deck and took my time, not intent on breaking his morning silence. He was in his thirties. The skin of his face was textured, and a reddish beard was advancing from whiskers to full. A loose-bound bale of blond dreadlocks gave shape to the hood that encased him. He glanced at me through thin slits.

"Have you counted the deer down there this morning?"

I looked down the hill and indeed, there were deer. I also saw that I had marred the view with our tent.

He continued to look at me from the corner of his eyes. "There are six," he concluded, and then, squeezing one eye shut, he pulled back the string of his imaginary bow and loosed his lethal arrow.

Suddenly he dropped his cloak, arched backwards onto his hands, and flipped back to his feet—a warped cartwheel.

"I'm learning Capoeira," he explained as he hopped from foot to foot. "You came with Angelo yesterday evening? I was on my way back from Grass Valley, and got in late."

I introduced myself.

"Cool, I'm Constance. Derek and I are business partners."

We walked towards the sounds of morning activity. Near the driveway, Constance bent and picked up a compound hunting bow that had been carelessly left in the grass. He cursed under his breath about people failing to care for his possessions and unclipped an arrow. "Do you like archery? I'm getting into bow hunting."

This confirmed my suspicions about his involvement with the Merry Men and I stood back and watched as he took aim at a series of crude targets set up against the hill on the high side of the driveway. He took several powerful breaths and closed his mind— his face was a conflict of grim relaxation. He loosed the arrow and missed the target, but not too badly.

"Here you go," he asserted, pressing the device into my hands. He walked around me and pressed a fist into my lower back, tapped my front shoulder, cocked my head, realigned my arm, and pressed my lower back again. "Ok, take three deep breaths and on the third exhale allow your eyes to relax. You need to stay firm, but loose everywhere. Completely present both here and with your target, but without thought too. It's very meditative… watch your lower back."

I became flustered and shot wide. The string snapped against my forearm, which instantly announced its repercussions with a crimson patch and a sharp burning sensation.

Constance chuckled, "Yeah, you need one of these." He pulled up his sleeve to reveal a leather gauntlet. He nodded towards the bow in my hand. "If it is something you want to do, you can do it. You just need to go for it."

His last words pricked me. They spoke of more than just archery. They articulated the hunch I had about the California pot country.

5

The girls proved to be an excellent source of information for my urgent curiosity during the first few days before the employers got used to us. The girls saw us as their charge—young and potentially wayward fledglings in need of strict education in the ways of work and culture.

Their tutelage began the first moment when we sat down in our canvas chairs in the morning sun. They heard our story, raised incredulous eyebrows, and dismissed it with simple responses.

"You guys are lucky. It is hard to find work if you are inexperienced."

I told them of the young circus in Garberville that Adrienne and I had watched being carried off to fortune.

Katherine, the dominant spokeswoman, replied, "Well yeah, you can find some super wack scene where they feed you, like, hotdogs and chips, and under-weigh your buds... ok, ok, ok, what are you guys doing? First lesson: while you talk, you should always be trimming. Every second is money. Keep your scissors moving all the time."

Adrienne and I both jumped up to equip ourselves with floral scissors, plastic trays, and jars of vegetable oil.

Sienna raised her eyes and studied our moves as her own shears snicked away leaves. "You might want to pull the springs out of those Fiskars, they will slow you down."

I hurried to denude my snips of their spring.

Katherine resumed without looking at us as we fumbled, hoping to mimic the girls.

"You can totally find work, but there are lots of guys now who are just paying fifteen bucks an hour or one-hundred-fifty a pound. One of my girls got talked into helping these dudes from the Bay who set up a grow, and these guys dropped them off at this big tent in the middle of nowhere with, like, a few gallons of water and a bunch of canned food and then just left them for three days. There was no toilet, no heat, like, absolutely nothing. Isn't that fucking terrible? Ok, that was extreme, obviously. I mean, most places are totally chill, but you just have to know what you're doing. So you guys should feel lucky that you found a good scene. Ummm... at that pace, you're going to trim, like, twenty buds a day, you can't spend too long on any one bud. I spin it once and then into the tub. Train yourself to pick out the crows feet, they don't want any crow's feet here, and just even out the calyxes—you don't want to mow them."

Penelope leaned over smiling sweetly and used the tips of her scissors to point at the bud I was holding. "Those little stem-looking things that split into three... those are crow's feet. This leafy part that looks like a teardrop and makes it bushy, that is the calyx. That is good stuff but it has to look even."

I thanked her and tried to get a grasp on the anatomy of the weed. I had seen plenty of marijuana, but somehow never grasped that it didn't grow in the tight little green nuggets presented during a sale. Neither had I contemplated that someone had handled each and every bud and given it a haircut.

"All the weed sold is trimmed first?" I blurted.

Katherine shrugged, "Basically, if you want to sell it on the market, at least."

Angelo eventually ambled up looking groggy. He stretched, and the base of his hairy belly peaked out from below his t-shirt. He plopped down in a chair and guzzled water.

"So how do you know Derek and Constance?" Sienna asked him. Her tone was subtle, and I had the vague impression that this question was important.

"Oh man, I've known those guys forever. I grew up with Constance and we met Derek and Isaac when we were all touring with The String Cheese Incident. We sold grilled cheese sandwiches out of a van one summer to pay for gas and tickets."

Sienna snorted. "Derek and Isaac toured with String Cheese? I thought they were rebellious Christian boys from Kansas."

Angelo laughed loudly. "They were, but that was a decade ago, before they found psychedelic rock. Isaac used to have dreadlocks, and they both had beards. Wouldn't guess it now, would you? Derek owns a Chevy dealership in Wichita with his brother."

Sienna lifted her eyes, clearly impressed by this trivia.

Apparently, the information resolved some unspoken question within the circle. My interpretation was that Angelo had taken his rank in the hierarchy. He was a longtime friend of the boss, which placed him on a special level. There might have been some resentment or tension with the arrival of the new force—this unknown entity who might disrupt the power balance. But it was clear that Angelo had no interest in hierarchy as long as they let him play Grateful Dead music from time to time on the sound system. And so the tension subsided. The unexpected benefit was that Adrienne and I were now somehow vouched for. It was Angelo's unspoken right as a childhood friend and not simply an industry relation, to bring transients. We were thereafter accepted, if not elevated.

"OK, lesson two," Sienna practically shouted, disrupting

Penelope from her bubbly expansion on sound-wave healing, and halting Adrienne in her tracks. "No cherry picking!"

Everyone stopped, which seemed monumental since it broke rule number one. They all starred at Adrienne in angered disbelief. She was standing by the plastic bin full of untrimmed colas (the big stems full of tightly clustered buds), clutching several healthy batons.

"Go ahead... help yourself to all of the heavy, nice buds. We will deal with all the loose, larfy shit you leave," Sienna continued, her eyebrows lifted in disgusted shock.

"She doesn't know!" said Penelope, finally getting the words out with effort, her brow furrowing with emotion.

"It's common sense, Pen. She shouldn't need to be told *that*."

Pen was offended and took to moping. Sienna turned her attention back to Adrienne, as if chastising a naughty child. "You don't sort through the bin and find the heaviest, biggest buds and take them for yourself. You take a mix. That's all."

Sienna resumed trimming in a huff and Adrienne returned to the bin trembling. She selected some sparse stocks then bolted back to her chair. Angelo put on his headphones and began to hum softly. The tension was too great however, and Sienna had to try for another closure now that the circle was damaged.

"I'm sorry, ok? It's just that cherry picking is the one thing that really gets to me. I mean, you didn't know, so whatever. Just don't cherry pick."

We all pouted for a while.

6

Shortly before the lunch break, Isaac assessed our work and returned a few trimmed nugs for further attention.

"They look pretty good for your first time, but you are slow. That's ok... just try to pick up the pace." He glanced at my pruning scissors. "Those are part of the problem. You notice how sticky they get? You have to clean them. Get some vegetable oil and keep it in a little jar. If it builds up like that, scrape the scissors and then clean them with a paper towel and oil. Are the girls explaining things to you?"

As there was no hasty response, I admitted they were. Adrienne remained silent and focused on the new activity of cleaning scissors.

"Keep the scissor hash!" said Pen with an excited wiggle. "It's nice to smoke!" She indicated a little brown ball she had been working on.

Adrienne removed the brown residue with a razor blade that Pen handed her, and offered her scissor hash as a thank you.

"Well, there is salad in the yurt if anyone wants lunch," said Isaac. "And Derek and Constance want to meet with you guys after you eat to explain our policies."

I nodded.

We ventured through the portal into the other world of the yurt, making sure to kick off our shoes. We spent several moments adjusting to the comfort and convenience, but then abruptly departed for the real world again when Constance called us out to see the rattlesnake he had decapitated behind the shed.

"I haven't seen many since the days started to get cooler, but I guess they're still around."

I wandered back into the yurt for salad and kombucha and had the same jarring culture shock, then returned to the sun-littered wilderness to watch a coyote chase a deer across the slope. Angelo seemed to share my bewildered sentiments and walked next to me to look down the hill at where the wildlife had disappeared.

"Yep. You get it all here! Except for a toilet. The lack of a toilet reminds you that you are out in the woods."

Adrienne and I joined Derek, Constance, and Isaac on the viewing deck, which turned out to be the conference room as well. Constance sat cross-legged, Isaac squatted with a foot forward as though he might spring up and take off running, and Derek remained standing, prepared for a formal address.

"All right, guys. So, you can stay as long as we have work. We wouldn't normally do this just so you know, but Angelo brought you and you guys seem nice and we see that you are making an effort."

Despite the words, his tone sounded like all business to me. I imagined that it was stressful to operate a marijuana grow. Constance didn't seem like the type to adopt the stress, so I supposed that role had fallen to Derek. I decided not to hold it against him.

"Well, we really appreciate the opportunity," I said. "So we will do whatever we can to help you guys." I had determined it was a good time to express our commitment.

"Well, just keep trimming then," Derek replied without humor. "We pay two hundred dollars a pound, and we expect you to trim about that every day. It might make for some long hours while you get the hang of it. We might have a little land work too. We pay twenty bucks an hour for that. We have enough hot water for everyone to shower every other day, so just work that out with the others. We will probably keep the crew we have for the rest of the work. Might be a couple others who show up here and there, but we expect the eight of you to get through the majority of the work... And, of course, I don't think I need to discuss privacy matters, but I'll mention them. No pictures of the land with plants, or photos of people with plants, and basically, just don't talk about this with people. We're putting a lot of trust in you guys."

We nodded solemnly.

Derek looked at Constance. "Anything else to add?"

Constance thought for a moment with his head bowed to his chest and then popped up onto his haunches with his palms pressed rigidly to the deck and howled across the valley like a wolf. He grinned at us. He looked a bit wolfish.

7

We were joined by Mandy and Shay that afternoon, and the circle was complete. Mandy was Isaac's girlfriend. She had come out from Kansas for Isaac, not the scene, and she preferred the world inside the yurt. Shay was a silent and sad-eyed druid. She preferred the world outside of the yurt. Sienna had ginger-colored hair, and danced with fire. And spoke it on occasion. Pen was so bubbly that everything about her conformed to it—from her curly hair to the round, dimpled cheeks that puffed out whenever she gave her wide-eyed smile. Pen played a gong when she wasn't trimming weed. The circle was round, but Katherine sat at the head—she was an unapologetic authority on everything. And we were Angelo's children.

"Yep, brought my kiddos along," he said with a smirk and a chuckle when Katherine defined us as such.

The name stuck and we remained under the paternal protection of Angelo's Dead Head calm. Adrienne and I were both ok with that.

The heat settled in for the afternoon and I focused on focusing. It was hard not to space out and simply twirl the little green balls in my fingers or become overwhelmed by the endless pile sitting on my tray. Penelope had shown me how to break the larger colas down into individual buds and then find a rhythm. The sweat trickled from my armpits down my sides, and my fingers adhered to everything they came in contact with, making it difficult to handle the buds.

"Try to hold the stem and not the bud. You don't want to rub the crystals off," reminded Katherine.

I had to clean my scissors every few buds, and the new bin that Isaac delivered seemed to be nothing but thin, loose buds with no real weight. Those turned into a small pile of plant litter when approached by snips, which the girls referred to as *larf*.

"Sorry, guys, but we gotta get through this Purple Urckle before we can start the White Rhino."

There was a chorus of groans, and Isaac shrugged, Sorry.

I wondered how many hours it would take to turn this flimsy fluff into one pound. I imagined working at this day in and day out for three months and felt sick. I tried to wipe my hands, but the paper towel came apart and adhered to the black goo on my fingers. I growled and cursed and wondered why I had ever thought this was a good way to make money.

I wasn't the only one feeling resentment. Shay suddenly let out a baleful wail and threw her tray to the ground (with enough care not to disturb the organization of her trimmed buds) and stood in protest. "I can't handle this heat! I've never been to a trim scene where they didn't have a covered space to work! Aaahhh!" She stomped towards the slope, turned her back on us, and commenced a session of frustrated yoga.

"You can go into the yurt, you know," said Mandy, sardonic and without sympathy. "Or the aluminum tent. There's a couch in there."

I could feel the tension rising again.

"I hate the yurt," was the response.

"Well you don't have to stay. Nobody is forcing you to eat the food or make great money. There are plenty of granola camps around," Mandy snapped.

Angelo turned up the volume on his headphones.

I decided I had nothing to complain about. I could endure some heat.

8

At dusk, Constance led a yoga session on the viewing deck and we sat in a circle and chanted, holding hands and offering three atonal *Ommms* to the universe. My body was not accustomed to sitting cross-legged and I found myself distracted from the spiritual uplift of the moment by the knots of pain in my back, hips, knees, ankles, and spleen. But I was impressed that everyone joined willingly, except Derek, who was still in the field working. Probably because he wouldn't be caught dead chanting *Oms*.

This ceremony turned out to be a daily ritual that was followed by a brief period of play where Constance demonstrated his developing skill at Capoeira, and Sienna instructed us in Acro-Yoga. Really, we all just flopped around like dying fish. We performed this ungainly dance until Isaac finally yelled from the yurt that it was time to eat.

Adrienne and I washed the dishes again, intent on demonstrating our appreciation to our new employers, and then wandered back to the tent beneath the burning stars, accompanied by the hungry eyes. We settled in between the rocks, to shiver ourselves into a restless sleep until another full moon rose and the sorrowful choir lifted their voices.

Book One

Part 3

1

Living and working with this peculiar community became normal right away. The outside world seemed far removed, and there was no reason to think about it. Adrienne and I had no needs, everything was provided: shelter, food, community, experience, and the sense that we were part of something. The nights were cold and the toilet was a hole in a little wooden hut, but even that had a great view. We all complained about the daily routine, but there was nothing to take issue with. We were being well paid to sit and talk and laugh and share our knowledge and stories.

The days rolled together as they tend to do under the conditions of routine and repetition. We trimmed, and trimmed more. We worked through the Purple Urckle, blasted through the White Rhino and White Widow, finished off the Trainwreck, had a spell of Mendo Purps, and settled into Blue Dream. The plants were happy that season and they produced in abundance as a show of gratitude. The days were warm and sunny and the air at night stayed dry. We weren't finding much *botrytis* mold or powdery mildew. The growers were confident and quietly overjoyed with the crop's success, and their satisfaction spread to the workers, so the entire milieu was buzzing with excitement.

And there was also the fear. It was 2008. George W. Bush was playing out his final months in office and making his final moves. Some of the old-timers say it was the last big year of busts. The stories were certainly there to support it. Humboldt County was alive with action, and every few days one of the neighbors would rumble down the driveway and disappear into the shed with Derek and Constance to share what they had heard about the latest raid out near Shelter Cove or up at Myers Flat.

The stories made it to our ears, too.

"Don't worry," said Katherine, "they never arrest people. And if they do, it's the owner. They just make the workers leave. Sucks, you lose everything you worked for, but at least you don't have legal fees added on top of it."

I wasn't worried. To me, the threat of a bust added to the excitement. It imbued just the right touch of danger for a young man enchanted with the idea of adventure and the possibility of being involved in activities that played out on the edges of society and unknown underworlds with positive, rather than sinister, goals. The situation was so surreal that my mind could not conceive of repercussions. There was no possibility of failure. And I was supported by like-minded others. Clearly, many believed in what we were doing and supported my growing conviction that there were other ways to live, alternatives to an unsatisfying paradigm that reigned in the world at large. I was not alone, and so I was not afraid.

When the first fly-over happened, I felt no terror or desire to bolt. I felt no guilt about what I was doing. I couldn't see any evidence that marijuana was hurting people, and I had nothing to lose. So I simply kept working, although my mind raced with the exhilaration.

"Keep your head down," cautioned Isaac when we heard the helicopter blades beating the air and drawing nearer the ridge. "Don't look up and they can't get photos of your face. And don't try to get up and go to the yurt, it makes it look like you are hiding, and that makes us look guilty. We just act like we are supposed to be here and don't care. We have our Medical Cards on the hill where they can see them."

Despite his outer calm and boyish smile, I could hear the tension in Isaac's voice. If the plants were cut and the camp shut down, as manager he stood to lose a lot more than I did. He was telling us the protocol, but I wasn't convinced he believed it was the best approach.

The helicopter appeared over the ridge. It wasn't as close as it sounded, but it could certainly see all it wanted to see. I tried not to watch.

"We have the legal number of plants," Isaac said reassuringly, more to himself than to us, "as long as they don't see the Guerilla Garden."

There were three flyovers while I was there, and near the end, there was a bust in the area but nobody in the neighborhood knew whose operation got hit or how badly they had been breaking the rules. Constance, who never showed fear or concern, stated that we weren't big enough to draw attention and that everything on the land—besides the Guerilla Garden—was close to legal.

"There are a lot of other people who the cops want to mess with before us."

He was right. On our farm, the helicopters and stories never amounted to more than anxiety.

2

Some days, Constance would pull me out of the circle to work with the plants. I secretly hoped for that scenario every day. There were endless tensions in the circle, and it wore on me. It seemed natural as we spent all day, every day, together that, at some point, differences of opinion would lead to bruised egos. But I also discovered that I was not destined to be a great "three pounds a day" trimmer that the girls swore was totally doable. If it was a reality somewhere, it was never going to be me. I was a "one-pound-in-twelve-hours" kind of guy and I wasn't seeing a whole lot of improvement. Adrienne was speeding up, but I hit a plateau almost immediately and I was realistic about it. Not everyone is a good trimmer.

After a couple of days working among the plants with Constance, I realized I could work a ten-hour day, as opposed to a twelve-hour day, and make the same amount of money and get some exercise as well. And working with the man of many hats was hardly dull.

Derek was the severe father; Isaac was the comforting mother; and Constance was... what was he? Constance was Northern California. He was the embodiment of the opportunity to be your dream, to be anything you could imagine. Constance stayed in a tipi on an outcropping of rock not far from our tent. The first day we worked with the plants, he took me in the Rhino, which was a caged, all-terrain vehicle with two seats and a small bed for hauling. I was hardly in my seat when he stepped on the gas and we skidded down the dirt track. I glanced at my driver from the corner of my eye as I braced myself against the frame—his face was set with unflinching focus. We reached a switchback and he pulled the e-brake and cranked the wheel, leaning his body to the inside of the turn. The Rhino slid in a harsh whip and threatened to carry us off the road and down the steep, grassy slope that loomed menacingly on my side. Just as we reached the point of disaster, he engaged the gears and we lurched forward onto the next straight, leaving a wake of dust hovering in the air. He did a J-turn at the next corner too, and then accelerated through a curve and took us over a bump-turned-jump with more than ample speed. I felt my stomach try to escape my mouth before it was forced back into its proper place by the impact.

"Let's do that again," Constance said moodily. "We can definitely get more air than that."

A half hour later, I staggered from the Rhino, a bit dizzy and shaky at the knees, but not disappointed.

"You want to see my tipi?"

Since we were parked right outside his abode, it was clear that was what we would do whether I wanted to or not, so I said I did, and he showed me his accommodations and his shrine.

Constance had a small table crowded with crystals and feathers, and interesting pieces of wood. He told me stories of how he had come across most of them, and in so doing recalled that he had seen a hawk down by a big oak several times in the last few days, and so we set off to look for feathers. We didn't find any, but we found the tracks of wild pigs that he was interested in tracking because they lead to mushrooms and also, if he knew where they congregated, he could hunt them. So we plunged into the valley and got lost amid the redwoods.

By the time we got to work with the plants, the sun was westering and we had a bundle of wild herbs to take to the kitchen, and a few rocks he was sure he could transform into arrowheads.

The next day I went to work in the cannabis garden again. But instead of going down the hill towards the garden, we loaded two mountain bikes in Isaac's truck and he drove Constance and me up to the top of the mountain to check the spring box. We looked at the valves and pipes near the spring, and examined the water tank, but I got the impression that Constance wasn't concerned about them.

"All right, these are fine. Let's bike down to the garden!"

Constance leapt upon the bike and sprang away down the hill. I watched the pile of blond dreads lift from his head before he disappeared. I followed him, lurching through the tall grass, and pinching the brakes with sweaty palms. I reached the steeper slope just in time to watch him fly sideways from his bucking bicycle and tumble through the grasses. He looked up the hill and raised his arms high in the air, letting out a mighty cry of triumph. Then he remounted and disappeared again. By the time I reached the garden, Constance was building rock towers with assiduous concentration.

3

One day early in our second week of residence at the farm, I was surprised to be pulled from the circle, not by Constance, but by Derek. It was time for the final harvest. He wanted to take down everything except for a few choice plants.

"Temperature might drop below freezing tonight and there's a possibility of rain tomorrow. I don't want to take any chances when things have been going so well. All the plants are ready anyway."

I hopped into his truck, pondering negative degrees in the tent, and we rumbled down the track and across the slope to the main garden.

The growing plots were well hidden from the yurt, and when standing among the plants and peering out at the surrounding hills, you could well believe you were the only person in the world. It was always warm in the garden and it had a cozy atmosphere. One could wander between the plants, going about their work, and feeling pleasantly lost, despite the small space. My expectation of a weed farm had been field upon field of plants stretching into the distance, but quaint reality turned out to be seventy plants in the main garden, thirty in the second garden further along the slope, and ten more in the slightly less official Guerilla Garden tucked into a small ravine on the backside of the hill.

My time of warm afternoons lost in verdant foliage was ending that day.

"All right. Let's strip as many fan leaves as we can and then take everything trim-able when it dries." Derek tossed me a pair of gloves.

I didn't enjoy wearing gloves when working with the plants, but fingers become so sticky that it's difficult to let go of whatever I was holding. I circled around each plant, yanking off the large fan leaves that sprang out from the colas, and wondered what these guys did in the off-season. We had worked through much of the garden and the ground was a carpet of leaves by the time I had the courage to ask any questions.

"So, will you head back to Kansas when all this is done?"

Derek was inspecting a bud and took his time before answering.

"Man, this is the third harvest on some of these plants, these colas were hardly developed when we cut the first round, and now the plants look like they haven't been cut at all. Not all years go this well. We've been pretty lucky... Yeah, I'll go back to Kansas."

I looked at the stock he was holding—a long spiky tube of green bubbles and warts. *What a weird looking plant to gain the love and hate of so many people,* I thought.

I kept working, though every leaf I touched clung to my gooey, resin-covered gloves and I spent more time trying to detach the leaves from myself than from the plants.

Then, to my surprise, Derek continued. "I like what's going on out here. People can be what they want to be and that is great, I don't know where else you can do that if you are the type who doesn't really fit into society, but I guess I'm not interested in changing myself enough to be one of those people. I'm not running from something or looking for something. You know what I mean? Ok, I used to run around and follow some jam bands with my buddies, but some people just keep going down the new road they discovered and some people go back to what they had. I like Kansas, the folks are pretty conservative, but they are good-hearted and things don't change much. I guess I like that consistency. It's not like that here. Too many unknowns."

Derek was industrious and moved to another plant as he talked. He smelled the plant and inspected the buds with the squint of an expert going through the routine. There was no emotion directed towards the plants, no singing to them as Constance did when he worked around them.

Suddenly, Derek sighed and let go of the plant and looked across the garden. "It's just so fuckin lucrative. I was growing herb in a garage back home for years and it was never more than money on the side. This though, if you have the energy and the resources, you'd be a fool not to do it. Think about that, man, you're young. Work down here a couple of years, save what you make, and get a little piece of property. If you know how to do a hard day of work, then you are set. I don't know how long it will last, but now is the time."

He studied me and I decided not to mention that I wanted to buy a motorcycle with my profits.

"Well, I'm not coming back again," he finally said. "Lucrative or not, the stress gets to me, and I just want to build up my business and start a family with my wife. Did you know I was married? And have a car dealership? Constance talked me into all this because I have a lot of experience growing. He needed my help, and the money is just too good to pass up. I don't regret it, but I'm not like him. Constance fits this place. He wants the adventure and freedom. He's not as traditional as me, and I guess he isn't afraid of the risk."

Derek was still watching me. I made an effort to show him I was fervently working, but he didn't seem to care.

"Funny how you can be in a place where everyone is different from one another and still not fit in."

4

We chopped down most of the plants, taking huge sections at a time and leaving only a series of spindly sticks protruding from the stock. We had several truckloads and Isaac and Constance joined us at the shed to break the stems down and hang them to dry. I was surprised at how quickly we took down the whole garden. I stopped as I walked up the hill towards the yurt and looked down at the patch. I was far enough away that the plants were shapeless masses on a bare patch of earth. It looked more like a cemetery than a garden. And it made me sad. It seemed that when the plants were growing, everything was growing and expanding and improving. Now it felt like everything had stopped, as if the fuel had run out. It struck me at that moment that the notion wasn't so far off the mark. Once the weed dried and we trimmed the last round, the work would be done. The work was the fuel driving the whole little community and there would be no need for us to remain. In fact, we would become a burden. I decided not to think about it. I turned my back on the cemetery and ran up the hill to the circle where my new friends were laughing and working and where everyone felt successful and fortunate.

5

The farm had two guests that day. One was a very tall, handsome girl in hot-pink tights, high-cropped jean shorts, and a mesh-back baseball cap. She joined the circle and I was told she was an *all-star* trimmer.

"She is like three people," Katherine said knowingly, then mock-glared at the new girl.

The girl was unaware we were talking about her. She had headphones in and was thrusting her chin forward rhythmically to the music, which was clearly fast paced. She looked intent on her prey, and her scissors were something of a blur. I hurried back to work feeling behind. First, the graveyard, and now a warp-speed trimmer. My mind conjured an empty warehouse at sunset. No matter how sad the consideration of leaving, the irony was that you wanted to work as quickly as possible in order to make more money in less time and get your share. There were others who would happily trim the buds before you got around to them.

The all-star suddenly whipped one of the headphones from her ear. "Yo, can I get some coconut water?"

It was said to no particular person, and it was more of a command than a request. Isaac sprang to his feet from where he had been lounging with a leg over the armrest, and ran to the yurt. Clearly, she was used to controlling her space.

The other guest was a tall, square-shouldered guy with a blond goatee and a ball cap sitting low over his eyes. He was also trimming, although he seemed far less concerned with his work than with finding willing ears for his tirades. He was invested in a nonsensical argument with Sienna and Katherine.

"Ok, you haven't been to Burning Man, so don't talk shit until you know what it's all about!" Katherine's voice was scathing.

Apparently, he had touched a nerve. He spit a line of snus into a can and smirked. "Nahh way, man, everyone talks shit about things they haven't seen. I don't have to go there to know it's wasteful. It's just not sustainable," he drawled in a languid voice. "Everyone up in these hills are all talkin like they're super conservationists, but then they turn around and burn a bunch of gasoline at a festival because they like to see fires. I can make fires too. I use them to heat my cabin, and I chop all the fuckin wood for it. And the only gasoline I need is to run my chainsaw. All these fuckin hippies aren't actually sustainable like they claim."

Katherine and Sienna were both too livid to find words and so their combatant continued at his measured pace.

"What we all should really be doing is getting plants in the ground and setting up solar panels, and getting some serious personal infrastructure set up. I'm all about seceding. We don't need a government out here; we have all the resources we need. I know ten guys I could call right now if I needed to build a road, and we would have that shit knocked out in a day and running tractors on veggie oil and everything. People out here know how to take care of themselves and one another. We got it all right here! But it's not all that festi bullshit where everyone's just preaching."

Katherine finally found her words. "Well that's a nice big truck you are driving!"

He chuckled. "Guy's gotta have his truck." This seemed to have reminded him of something and he craned his head around and whistled, "Drew! Get over here, boy!" There was some thumping and some awful scraping and I turned to see an enormous bloodhound slide from the bed of his truck and do it's best to run over. Drool streamed from beneath its jowls and, as if he and his master had some understanding, Drew passed Katherine at close range and delivered a smear of slobber across her knee.

"Ugh. Fucking disgusting!" she fumed and found no option but to excuse herself for cleansing.

The goateed anarchist considered that a victory. "That's a good boy, Drew. That's a gooood boooy!" He cooed and smirked, relishing the antagonism.

6

That night, a small party was held to celebrate the final harvest. We all called it a day when the sun was nearing the mountain peaks and we gathered at the viewing deck to practice our Acro-Yoga, creating monstrous eight-legged shadows on the hillside behind. I wasn't particularly fond of this daily exercise, but the girls were and they smiled sweetly and explained that I would become hooked if I gave it a chance. I spent most of the time lying on my back, wincing as the gravel in the driveway prodded my spine, and wincing as the girls tried to balance on my up-thrust legs, stretching my muscles to unfavorable extremes. I looked over at Angelo who had been allotted the same position as me. He looked absurd on his back with his legs held perpendicular to the ground. Neither of us was flexible enough to hold our legs straight and I thought we resembled dying insects. To make things worse, Angelo, who was somewhat stouter than me, was trying to support Constance, who was bigger than us both, but he wanted to be on the aerial team. Finally, Angelo's leg produced a loud and unappreciative popping noise and we decided it was sufficient exercise for the day. The sun drained away to the sounds of our carefree laughter and Angelo's feeble groans.

Sienna and Penelope taught us the art of belly dancing that evening, and Constance picked up a guitar he was learning to play. It was tuned to a key he had designed himself and he accompanied our efforts with the anguished yowling of a misused instrument. Derek walked in, glanced our way, grabbed a beer from the cooler, and fled. The rest of us collapsed in fits of giddy laughter. I laughed with personal delight because I noticed how comfortable everyone was, spending time with one another after hardly more than a week of acquaintance. Shay was no longer clinging to the shadows, and Isaac and Mandy, who generally retired shortly after dinner, were curled up on the couch, giggling.

We were through the portal of the other world with white carpets and large-screen televisions, so Adrienne and I made popcorn and the whole crew got stoned and watched cartoons. It felt like home. If you wanted to be there, then you belonged.

Book One

Part 4

1

And there it was. In the midst of it all, when the routines were stable and the flow established, it suddenly stopped.

The day was warm and we sat in our normal chairs in our normal places, which we had unconsciously adopted. We were digesting quinoa salad and pushing through the post lunch sleepiness when Isaac appeared and abruptly announced, "Let's try to finish up this strain. This is the last day, so make a push until about five and we can add up numbers and pay you for all your help."

And just like that, everything began to crumble.

"But... we still have to trim a whole strain... the Green Goddess," said Sienna, unable to think of anything else to say.

Isaac shrugged apologetically. "The guys made the decision. Don't ask me."

Nobody else responded. The news that we were done came as a surprise to us all, and the silence of resentment settled on the group. We brooded and skulked. We weren't sure whether to slow our work in protest, or to push on and make as much money as we could on our remaining half day.

Our personal reflections persisted until Katherine bluntly dropped her tray at her feet in order to illustrate her opinion, and then underlined the action with a few choice words: "Fuck this! They still have all of the Green Goddess, and tons of Sour Diesel from the second harvest. If they don't want us here, I am going to pack up."

I wondered how we could feel so much agitation, but we all did—with the exception of Mandy who would stay regardless, and maybe Angelo who was imperturbable.

Shay looked mortified. "They told me there was enough to make five thousand dollars. I'm not even halfway! *Pffff.* I don't know what I'm going to do now, or where the fuck to go!"

It was as though we had all forgotten there was a world outside. We had forgotten that this could, and indeed would happen. The news had been abrupt, certainly, but like the others, I had a feeling as if I'd been wronged. They'd taken away my rights. I had the irrational idea that I deserved to be there, but I was being thrown out of my own home. I had contributed, I had given my energy, worked hard, and now I was being turned out. I began to think about the money I had been working towards, adding numbers in my head. I became convinced I would be underpaid. I forgot about the three organic meals I ate daily, and the craft beers I drank, and the hot showers and evenings watching movies under piles of blankets in the yurt. The generosity had been too great, and when it was stripped away, the loss seemed offensive. I felt a weird switch from gratitude to feeling entitled—brought on by what? Being spoiled? By high expectations? By the rumors we'd been fed of flowing cash, and easy trimming, and three-pounds-a-day stories? Only a few weeks earlier, I'd hitchhiked to California with no place to go and no job prospects. Against all odds, I had been taken in and given everything I wanted, everything I could have dreamed of. Now, in spite of it all, I felt like I had been cheated and chased off.

I waited for them to return and tell us they had made a mistake, but it was only the entertainment of hope, which I knew was pointless. When Adrienne addressed our personal situation, it all became very real.

"So what are we going to do? We didn't plan how to get home."

Of course we hadn't. Who wants to go home after they've discovered paradise?

2

Our brooding was not graced with time, and so without opportunity to wish our favorite nooks and vistas farewell, we packed our tent and our sparse belongings and gathered at the yurt for the rather formal ceremony of payment. They doled out our due in plain white envelopes full of cash. As soon as I received my pay, my frustrations were suddenly forgotten and the eighteen hundred dollars I had earned for two weeks of work seemed like an open door to the world. It was far less than I had expected to walk away with, but those expectations had changed and evolved so quickly during my time of employment that they had become frail and uncertain, and the tangible cash simply erased any thoughts of what I had hoped for. The money in my hands was real.

Constance attempted to transform the occasion into something like a spiritual closure and herded us towards the viewing deck to hold hands and chant the good ol' three *Oms*, but after the hard feelings and the business of cash exchange, it seemed too forced, too contrived. After our atonal moaning was over, Constance eyed us, his wolf face held in a smirk. He could interpret the atmosphere. He sighed and leaned back.

"Sorry, guys, but it's all business in the end. We are here at the bottom line for money. And that goes for Derek and me as well. But the fun we had and the things we learned we can take with us when we go back into the real world."

Most of us nodded. Shay looked moody. "Why can't the real world just be like this?"

3

The real world was not that. I wandered the aisles of a grocery store in Trinidad, squinting under the fluorescent lights and watching people shop. They didn't pay any attention to one another; they just looked bored.

"I pity them," Sienna stated with a supercilious wrinkle of the nose.

Pen stopped reading the ingredient list on the jar of honey she was holding and looked at the store customers as though noticing for the first time that there were other humans present. After a glance, she resumed her study of the honey. "Why? They are no different from us. We are in the same store buying chips and ice cream." She replaced the honey and looked at the neighboring brand.

"You know what I mean, Pen," Sienna said. "Look at how unhappy everyone is. They are just so... empty."

"We don't know their stories. They might all be part of the same industry as us. It's easy to feel like an elite member, but maybe they are all farmers. Everyone looks unhappy in grocery stores. We can't really judge. In the end, all the people out in the hills working with marijuana are just people too, no better or worse."

"God, I wasn't looking for a moral lesson," Sienna muttered and walked away.

Penelope shrugged and sighed and replaced the honey, apparently deciding that it was too uncertain. I followed along pushing the cart and watching the shoppers go about their business. It was true, we were no better than anyone involved in other lines of work, but I had a suspicion there was something extra to the trade, something other than the legal status that made it unique.

I'd been adopted by Katherine, Sienna, and Penelope. Adrienne had headed north with Angelo, who could take her all the way home and who, by that point, we regarded as a saint. I had opted to stay a few more days after the girls told me there was the chance of more trimming for another grower they knew. They dragged me along like their kid brother and we made the journey up to Trinidad where Katherine had a house rented right on the coast and, in fact, had a small indoor grow of her own. This was further evidence to me that the cannabis industry was far reaching—not isolated to small operations in the hills. And that it probably ran in veins throughout various facets of society.

Trinidad was a sleepy, retired, slow-paced community, and still, amidst its mundane walls, marijuana was right at home, adaptable and willing to be part of any life that invited it in.

We ate our ice cream and chips and other junk food and watched movies in Katherine's big, strange house. I had been on the farm for only two weeks, but it had been so comprehensive that I felt foreign in all other situations. The yurt was as close to the "other world" as I needed to get. Katherine's house, with all of its amenities and space, felt drafty and excessive.

I diagnosed myself with culture shock and went to bed thinking of my friends and my community, and trying to blend them with my experience. I couldn't figure out why the Northern California industry seemed so removed and disconnected from my home. Oregon was not unfamiliar with weed; many people I knew were growing a plant or two. But there was a divide, something that made the wilds of Northern California different. The notion made me restless. I had always considered pot an activity— something people enjoyed as recreation. And I assumed that it came either from friends growing a few plants, or minor drug dealers, and was probably originally sourced in British Colombia or Mexico. Now I understood that the people growing marijuana were from my own larger community and culture, and realized there was something more to it than just growing and selling drugs. I had seen only one farm, but from the stories I'd heard about other farms, it seemed as if there was a lifestyle associated with the trade, a lifestyle that stood out from all others that surrounded it.

It irked me that I didn't know how to be a permanent part of that lifestyle, and it suddenly felt more inaccessible now than it had when I was hitchhiking down from Oregon two weeks earlier. Because of the plant's illegal status, the whole community was shrouded in secrecy and guarded by fear. This aspect would return to Oregon with me, and it bothered and excited me to be close to such a clandestine culture. I would have to keep this part of my life secret. I would have to lie to my parents. I would probably feel cool about my experience, but also protective and insecure about it. But what aggravated me most was that I didn't know if I could find my way back to it. The experience existed apart from my normal continuum of life.

As I drifted off to sleep, I told myself that it might be an isolated moment for now, but it was a seed, and surely it would grow.

4

We were invited for a day of trimming in the Eureka area. Already full of images and ideals, I imagined a townier version of the farm. A tidy little house with a well-vegetated backyard full of Buddha statues and chickens. But we pulled up at a dubious warehouse growing like a weed from wide fields of concrete. We summited a failing staircase, gingerly lifting the blackberry brambles from our shoulders, and rapped on the door. We were quickly ushered in and then the door shoved the daylight back outside.

The room was stifling, and the hum of dehumidifiers filled the chamber with the thick droning of dying wasps. The room was swaddled in black Visqueen plastic; the interior a demon butterfly chrysalis.

We were directed to vacant seats at one of the two long plastic tables, and a silent, bony-armed wraith outfitted us with trays and scissors and finally, with buds. The low-hanging work lamps cast tepid puddles of light on the dirty white tables, and beyond the glow, the room faded into the shadow of black plastic.

Sienna started coughing. "Oh god! This bud is totally covered in powdery mildew. I am so allergic to that shit!"

The chubby guy who had led us in rubbed his puffy eyes. "Yeah, it's been really bad, we've been running the dehums, but it just keeps spreading. Trim as much of it out as you can!"

His face was hairless and he wore a Dodger's baseball cap pulled down low on his round head, and an Adidas jogging jacket. "I want you guys to make it look as good as possible, but we gotta burn through this shit, so speed is everything. If you are hungry, there's some food on the table there. Thanks for coming guys."

I looked over at the food table. Bags of chips, two-liter bottles of Pepsi, and a can of baked beans on a little table coated in a film of dust.

Well, this is different, I thought.

There were twenty or more trimmers besides us, mostly independent, and mostly tuned into their personal music. A group of ten boisterous and jovial trimmers was at my table. Some of them had matching t-shirts with "Grind Crew" printed on the front.

"We have a van and a car, and we all tour for the whole season. We just move from scene to scene, sometimes for a day, sometimes for a week. People know us. We can work through a crop in fuckin no time!" one of the girls explained.

They were a motley group ranging from a boy who might have been an active member of his high school chess club when he wasn't trimming pot, to a gray and grizzled man missing his two front teeth, to a barefooted girl who peered through the mask of dirt on her face, and a tall, handsome lady with pristine dreadlocks and a careful arrangement of metal in her ears, lips, and nose. I asked the girl how they all met.

"Yo! This is our third season as a crew. We just met at different farms, and we can all just throw down at the trim table ya know? We are all like brothers and sisters!"

We worked for several hours and then Sienna said she would die if she had to breathe spores any longer. Katherine sighed and asked Pen and I if we were desperate to stay. I was enjoying the variation of conditions, but was also feeling paranoid and unhealthy, so with little discussion, we retired, were paid, and left.

Sienna was adamant about her opinion. "How can anyone work in those conditions? Did you see how filthy it was? I feel sick!"

Penelope smiled. "Remember that it's just business for a lot of people. Not everyone cares about the community. But that's ok, they offered us work and food and they were honest. So other than the setting, they weren't that different from the farm."

Sienna scowled. "Disgusting."

5

Then it was the off-season. There were no more leads. I couldn't stay forever, loitering at Katherine's house. So I stuck my thumb in the air and migrated north, my pockets full of cash and thoughts of adventure brewing in my mind. There was a world of opportunity. California would still be there next fall.

Book Two: The Nascent Culture (Fall 2009)

Part 1

1

Our shadows lunged, expanding into giants and then shrank to dwarves against the backdrop of bushes as we marched in circles around the maddened fire. We cried out at the top of our lungs to the starry sky and then, with no warning, Logan broke for the creek. With whoops of joy we all followed, and crashed into the still waters, turning the black glass to luminous foam with boisterous leaps. The extensive quiet around us endured our shrieks and bellows, but when we climbed shivering from the waters and filed back to the fire to crouch naked before it, the emptiness of the valley resumed its mastery and the clear air was buried by silence.

Brooke looked at us through the flames. His hair, matted into a sodden peak in front of his face, streamed water and cleaved his eyes apart, making them seem foreign to each other. He spoke in his unhurried country tone that, without effort, carried articulate pleasure and simple wisdom.

"Imagine trying to do this in your backyard in the city. Freak out all the neighbors. The police would be a-knockin at your door... Yep!" One of his eyes locked with mine while the other stared at the heart of the fire.

I could never figure out those eyes. There was no questioning in them. He was not studying me, or judging, or even wondering. All I could guess about those eyes was that they held some patient hope of recognition or familiarity with another soul that maybe, through a long gaze, we would discover we no longer needed words to express ourselves, that we could be understood through a simple look.

"Yep, we are free here," Brooke continued. "Everywhere else they would think we were lunatics or Satan worshipers." His mouth spread into a smile as he continued to watch me through the flames. "I just want to be peaceful and happy and live with nature and open my mind. I don't want to bother anyone. And here, when we feel like it, we can scream at the top of our lungs."

Kay and Logan responded to this by tilting their heads back and howling at the sky. With a great laugh, Brooke and I joined in until we all fell back in the sand giggling.

"And we sure are free to open our minds!" blurted Kay through a fit of chuckles. "Logan, pass that bag of mushrooms over here!"

Logan sat up as though he were spring-loaded and looked at us with an amazed smile on his face. I watched his hand stretch out beyond its traditional capabilities, and grope around for the paper grocery bag brimming with *Cyanescens* mushrooms. Logan dragged the psychedelics towards him with unnecessary effort while leering at us with a mischievous smile. He crammed several mushrooms into his mouth and thrust the paper sack towards Kay, who helped himself with glee.

"Here you are, Ben, you silly hen!" Kay said as he passed the bag my way.

"Oh boy!" I said, picking out a couple of choice mushrooms and handing the bag on to Brooke. "The world is already a strange place! Need it become stranger?"

The smoke of some bitter alien wood wrapped around my head, and Brooke's divided face seemed to shift. The mushrooms we had eaten previously were sending bubbles of distortion rippling across my mind, and every time I looked up, I was in a different place, looking at the fire from another perspective, occupying the locations and the energies of my friends. I felt like a student of the universe on my first day of class.

Brooke twirled a mushroom between his fingers and then popped it into his mouth. "I want the world to get as strange as it possibly can!" he said, and then let out a mighty whoop and we all leapt up with laughter to dance around the fire again.

2

The Tipsytom Valley lies somewhere between the ocean and the arid lands of the east, and honestly, I never was able to learn its whereabouts. In fact, I believe it moved from time to time, occupying different folds between the endless hills, relocating in order to sample new parts of the country, nestle in new places, always deep down, trying to get closer to the nurturing warmth of the earth's heart. Depending on where the valley was at the time, there were usually two to three approaches, all of them offering a variety of risks. No approach was paved until late in my career when the main road to Lassy earned its first blacktop, although even that was short-lived as a good two miles had tipped into the river by late fall.

During our first venture into the valley, we drove twelve hundred miles of logging roads in search of the lost dell and found the secret entrance only because Logan noticed the name of the valley spray-painted on the road in pale yellow with an arrow pointing down a washed-out hole between the trees. We followed the clue and some hours later emerged into the small paradise.

We didn't know what awaited us in that little scratch in the earth, only that there was a guy growing weed, and that he needed the help of at least one person and, we hoped, the help of three. My friend Logan Whitepyre had sniffed out the opportunity and offered that if there was work for one, then likely there was work for another. I felt confident given my experience the previous year, but also knew that Logan hoped for my commitment because we had purchased a car together for two hundred dollars, which necessitated that we remain within relatively close proximity.

"I know the peculiar way things work down there. Of course I'll go," I said.

And so we packed everything we could imagine needing: surfboards, hammers, a sewing machine, a straight jacket, and headed down the coast towards California. Our activities were no great secret, and several hours down the road our friend Kay Strider called.

"Are you dudes on your way to Cali?"

I looked at Logan with a raised eyebrow. "That's weird you should ask, Kay. As a matter of fact, we are. You have uncanny timing."

The pride dripped from his voice and I could tell he was fighting triumphant laughter. "So you guys have some trimming work?"

I looked at Logan again with two eyebrows raised this time. "Maybe. Nothing for sure."

I could hear him nodding. "Cool, I'm on a bus up from Santa Cruz. Can you guys snag me in Arcata?"

I replied with a grim laugh. "Whadya say, Logan? Should we rope Kay into this adventure? He is looking for work."

Logan laughed heartily and without surprise. "Where does he want us to pick him up?"

Over the course of a year, it had become quite a normal concept to head south for a season of trimming. I wasn't sure if it was only my friends who had discovered the incredible opportunities that lay south of us, or if the secret was out and prospectors were caravanning into the region from all corners of the country. There never seemed to be a great deal of discussion; it was just that everyone suddenly knew someone who had a grow scene.

"We are part of a migration, Logo."

He chuckled. "Let 'em come man, there is endless work down there. The whole country wants weed, and California is giving it to 'em."

I looked at the frothing ocean from the passenger window. "Yeah, until it gets too big and the government has enough."

Logan looked at me and winked. "That's the best thing about this industry. There are no expectations! It could be gone tomorrow!"

We retrieved Kay from a grocery store and he wedged himself into the back seat. Kay Strider, appropriate to his name, is the longest, lankiest fellow I have ever seen. His knees were obliged to spend time near his ears amidst the excesses of our preparations in the back half of the car. His lips parted in a smile revealing large horse teeth.

"Hey, Benji. Hey, Logo! Let's make some money. I'm broke!"

I revived my concerns for our new companion, and Kay tussled my hair from the backseat.

"Benji, we are years late on this stuff. The weed industry has been growing since ninety-six when they first made medical herb legal. We are just another batch late to the game. Let's be happy it's still an option."

Logan nodded, "Everything is uncertain. Everyone expects Obama to be chill about it, so it seems safer than ever, but who knows. They could crack down, in which case we are fucked. Or they could legalize it, in which case... we are fucked! So now is the golden moment!"

Deciphering the confusing and scribbled instructions, and drawing on a great deal of intuition, we turned towards the hills and urged our poor car, Helga, up the unbearable inclines. And then we drove, and drove, and drove some more, certain that we had driven off the map and into another dimension. It was late the following day when we bumped and bounded down the savage road and into the valley, rolling on a flat tire. So vicious were the roads in that region that we sustained two flat tires during our first week of residency, the second of which happened as we returned from fixing the first.

Upon reaching the valley, however, everything changed. We lurched out of the dirt and onto a gentle paved road that seemed to carry us along of its own accord, and so comfortable was it to drive that we nearly missed the gap in the bushes and the telltale orange marker that was our final clue. I backed up and Logan hopped out of the car, clicked some numbers into the padlock, and then dragged the heavy chain out of the way. I breathed deeply the fragrant air and smelled the pleasant strangeness of the valley. In that moment, I had the thought that I would see many things in this place.

Logan snapped his fingers before my vacant eyes when we

turned off the paved road and trundled down a dirt track until the trees parted and we had our first panorama of the Tipsytom.

Tipsytom was a small valley that had a feeling of great self-importance. It preferred to present itself as a mighty valley and did so by stretching its floor as flat and as far as possible before abruptly sending its walls straight up as high as they could reach. It jealously impeded all views of the larger, snowy peaks that lurked somewhere beyond and demanded that its own surrounding battlements be the highest points visible. With no boundaries to guide it, the middle fork of the Triumph River spilled in from the ruthless and minatory gorge above the valley, and instantly became lost amidst the Tipsytom's exaggerated flatness. The river wandered about from side to side searching for its way, or dividing into separate parties to scout the far edges of the plane before it happened upon the only available egress, and rushed back together to disappear into the ruthless and minatory gorge that lay below the valley.

The Triumph River had erased most vegetation in the valley during its questing, and the entire boastful flat was a barren labyrinth of gravel flood plains and bewildered sand bars. Only occasionally, on some shy promontory, could you see a clump of poplar trees flapping ludicrously in the light breeze, or along some subterranean spring was a streak of ash. Once Tipsytom threw its shoulder into the uplift of the surrounding hills however, vegetation seized the land. Colors had paled through the long summer months. The green of the trees had bleached, and the grasses had gone yellow. The ash and poplar and alder claimed the lowest benches of elevated land, covetous of the water near at hand. Then the manzanitas and the madrones tangled with the poison oak across the first healthy slopes before they gave way to the more mature heights where the fir forests overcame them all and only occasionally allowed a congress of pine or a crotchety old oak to reside. The sky seemed far away from the valley and expressed itself with aloof blue at the greatest of distances.

We stopped the car in the middle of the road and sat on the warm hood gaping at the proud little Tipsytom. So we hardly noticed when the lean and ragged homesteader approached and contented himself to watch us watch the valley.

"Yep yep yep! It's pretty nice," he said, gently drawing us out of the spell. "Welcome to my Shangri-La!"

3

The young man standing on the crest of the hill looked wild. His eyes darted between us and beyond us and never stopped moving. Only later, when they took the time to rest on the eyes of another human, did they find their ease and hope.

"One of you is Logan, I guess?"

Logan put on his professional smile and walked forward to shake hands. "You are Brooke then!"

The wild man nodded. "Yep, that's me!" he said with a simple smile and removed his hand to fidget with the couple of buttons left on his thinning plaid shirt. The buttons were fit into the wrong holes. His eyes continued to dart everywhere as we stood facing each other.

Kay and I introduced ourselves and told him straight away that we were looking for work in the area.

Brooke nodded, but didn't seem to pay attention. "Just so you know—there is a mountain lion living on the property. A mother with two cubs. She's been stalking me."

Our eyes widened.

"Well shit!" said Logan "That makes things exciting. Have you seen her?"

Instead of nodding, Brooke's eyes darted about even more emphatically. He pulled the lank hair away from his forehead and tugged at his dark beard, which hung to his chest.

"Yeah, at least twenty times. Two days ago, she cornered me against some bushes. I had only a bucket so I waved it in the air and yelled. She just looked at me and I could tell she was deciding whether to kill me or not. She just looked at me like cats do for about two minutes and then walked away."

We had no response to this, so Brooke continued. "It will be nice to have some company on the land, but if you guys are gonna stay, I thought I should tell you."

We left Helga parked at the top of the drive and followed Brooke down a steep track towards a tarp tent a couple hundred yards bellow. Brooke flopped along barefooted, swinging his arms like one who is accustomed to open spaces. His hair was a disheveled pile, and his beard a straggling nest. His shirt swung off one shoulder and he applied no effort to replace it. His trousers hung in ribbons.

It was not a long road, but Brooke kept stopping to speak and so we paused several times on the journey.

"I've been out here almost five months by myself. I go into town on occasion, but don't have much time, and I don't really like to leave the plants alone, so I stay on the land for the most part."

He flopped a bit further and then stopped again to address us. "Everything was pretty good until the cougar came. It was just me and the green ladies. Then one day, about a month ago, I think, I started to get creeped out, my skin would tingle and I would get the feeling that something was watching me. After that, I started to see tracks and scat. Then in the last couple weeks, I started to see her, just a few times, at a distance. But I think that was part of her plan. This week she seems to be everywhere I go. She doesn't even try to hide. She wants me to see her and to know she could eat me whenever she wants. I started to hear her outside my tent at night and notice her in the shadows when I was walking somewhere. So I pretty much stopped sleeping. I started to carry a machete, but every time I set it down somewhere for a few moments, that was when she would turn up. She's like a spirit."

Brooke looked across the valley. "This place is wild. I think there are only a few hundred people in the whole valley, and they are almost all in the village or on the road to Lassy. So other than the tavern over on the other side of the hill, there is no one close by."

Kay exacted a low whistle. "That's intense, man. I am glad you're ok."

Brooke stopped again and looked at us. His eyes were a blur of movement, but all else was calm. "Yeeahh, well, I know I'm on her land. It is more hers than mine. But she is playing mind games with me. She's been trying to drive me off, and every time I start to calm down, I look up and she's watching me. When she caught me by the bushes I thought it was over, and to be honest, if you guys hadn't turned up, I was thinking of leaving until someone could come. I have that feeling that she was going to get me in the next couple days. Yesterday, I was sure she was watching me all day."

Brooke turned and sprang down the rest of the drive in long bounds and went skidding into the open end of the tarp tent.

Logan gave me an incredulous look. He tended to disbelieve anything that resonated with the supernatural or that deviated from nature's patterns.

"Dude, nobody sees a cougar twenty times. Maybe he caught a

glimpse, but I think he has been alone in the wilderness too long! That's a good way to go crazy."

4

The tarp tent was a simple aluminum frame system running twenty by thirty feet. Brooke's little personal tent was tucked into a bush next to it. Those were the only structures on the forty-acre parcel. The slumped dirt driveway we had walked down, and which cut across a hillside of clay and long grass, was the only entrance to the property.

"There was a cabin here way back, but every fifty years or so there's a big flood, and the bench it was sitting on collapsed into the river and the whole thing was carried off. That's what the locals say," Brooke explained. "That was thirty years ago or more, and nobody has been here since."

The tent was poorly equipped. On one side, a woodstove squatted in the dirt, its pipe rammed through a sheet of plywood, which was the only wall section not made of plastic tarp. On the other side was a simple, waist-high workbench with organic canned goods and a little propane stove. There was a car battery, and a pile of tarp scraps and, hanging behind a tarp that separated the back third of the tent, was the early harvest: one precocious plant that had wanted cutting and now filled the area with the scent of hay.

"Pretty simple living here," I noted.

Brooke smiled, showing a bit of modest pride. "Yep, don't need much."

He led us along a path from the higher ground down to the river plain. We shouldered our way through a gap in a wall of thick bushes and emerged in the garden. The garden was on a glittering beach of sand and loose river stones that ran along a rather inviting creek. The plants were basking in the sunshine, each with ample personal space, spread across the beach in their individual pots constructed of ground cloth and chicken wire.

Brooke inspected one of the plants and inhaled with deep relish. "Ahhh! Good afternoon, ladies! How are you, my lovely darlings?"

For a moment, he seemed to forget about us and wandered among the plants, caressing them and smiling at them with fondness. "They have been my best friends out here all summer. I feed them and water them and sing to them." He looked up and his face paled. "And there," he muttered, "up against those bushes, is where the mountain lion trapped me."

I had no trouble believing Brooke's story. It didn't seem likely that a person could imagine a cougar crouched before them just fifteen yards away. But then, we had just met Brooke, and there was ample chance he was completely insane.

Brooke guided us along the beach path, which eventually veered away from the creek and into a low trough because, as we would realize in the future, the beach was in fact a flood channel. We crawled up a slope and through bushes to emerge in a small glade encased in the densest of brush where there were a dozen more plants. Brooke was still dwelling on the lioness.

"She watches me here too. I have seen a shape pass in front of the entrance twice while I was watering the guerilla garden. Ah, here's my machete, I was wondering where I had left that—Ahh! Oooh boy! And these, I forgot where these were too."

Brooke picked up a paper bag and stuffed his face deep into the opening. Then he looked at us with a smile, his eyes darting towards the entrance and around the garden. "I picked these last time I was up in Oregon. It was a great year for them last fall.

Almost three pounds when I brought them down in the spring, but I guess I am down to a few ounces!" He beamed at us.

Logan craned his neck and reached into the bag. He pulled out a dark and shriveled mushroom. "Ahh! Oregon Blues," he said quietly with a polite smile.

When Brooke turned to leave, Logan affected a perspicacious look and murmured to Kay and me beneath his breath, "Seeing cougars, huh? The puzzle is quickly coming together."

5

The following days elapsed in a psychedelic haze. We would wake in the cool morning air as the sun discovered old Tipsytom, and the sound of Brooke's rich and happy voice belted out Grateful Dead or Bob Dylan songs across the expanse accompanied by the strained tinkling of an old guitar dying of exposure.

We fed and watered the plants during the cooler morning hours and constructed a few simple furniture items out of scrap lumber—a table and a bench. And one day we dug a sizable latrine. But invariably, by mid-day, we were eating mushrooms and splashing naked in the creek, or tromping in the forest on the hillside, or through the thickets of the valley and startling the endless wildlife that seemed to regard us as an impossible band of mythical creatures rather than a threat.

Brooke smoked DMT from a bong most mornings at breakfast and would lie for several minutes laughing at the sky while tears of bliss streamed from the corners of his eyes. This added evidence to Logan's case—he was a determined opponent of the cougar theory, and regarded Brooke as pleasant, confused, and likely crazy. Indeed, we never saw the persistent lion or her cubs, although without discussion, we rigged trip-wires with bells and other alarms around our sleeping bags, and each night when we nestled into the sand on the beach where we slept, we pulled our machetes and hatchets close.

Several times Brooke stumbled into the pole tent after dark looking harried and disheveled, his beard a mess from his worrying, and his eyes like pin balls. He would exclaim that he'd seen her shadowy form and that we could not let our guard down. We would sit him down and Kay would roll him a joint, and then his eyes would steady and he would look at one or the other of us with his hopeful gaze.

6

Some days the four of us would pile into Helga and drive along the inappropriately quaint roads to find a good swimming hole on the Triumph River near the access to the ruthless and minatory gorge at the top of the valley, or near the ruthless and minatory gorge near the bottom of the valley. On these excursions, we never saw a soul.

There was evidence of other human beings in the Tipsytom, but only at night. Occasionally we could hear the muted sounds of music from the Tipsy Tavern on the other side of the large hill that protruded into the valley and formed one edge of our property. But the sounds came only when the door of the bar was open, and whenever it closed again, we sank back into silence. There were also a couple of lights that peered out from the forested hillside on the opposite slope of the valley. We assumed they must be residences, but there was no telling, and we had yet to see any tangible representative of our species.

Although no human life was visible, there was no shortage of wildlife on the roads. We had to take care at dusk to calm our young and masculine appetite for driving at arrogant speeds on the deserted and well-paved roads. Deer had a tendency to congregate on the far side of the blindest bends. During the day, squirrels would blow off the road like leaves in the wind when we swept down on them. We saw foxes and myriad birds, and even a coyote once, looking embarrassed that he had been spotted.

One evening, just after dark, Logan and Kay and I were driving back to the property down a winding road when we thumped over a long tubular object stretched across the track. Logan stepped on the breaks.

"Oh shit! We just ran over a snake."

He put the car in reverse and carefully backed up, making a wide curve along the shoulder. When we had retreated far enough, we saw it in the beam of our headlights. The sight turned my stomach. A rattlesnake was writhing violently on the pavement, a stretch of its midsection flattened, and viscera trailing out, staining the road.

Kay breathed in sharply behind me. "Oh god, we gotta do something about it!"

The three of us climbed out of the car and Logan started digging around the trunk searching for any tool with which to terminate the poor beast's suffering. I lingered near the car, unable to tear my eyes away. I had a terrible fear that in the snake's extreme state, it could suddenly lunge ten yards and strike one of us.

"There is nothing here," said Logan, and sighed with frustration. "The only thing I have is my pocket knife."

We stood paralyzed for a short time and finally came to the difficult conclusion that we must perform the grizzly task of driving over it one, and possibly several, more times when we heard a rumbling from up ahead. The glow of headlights grew across the trees. A moment later, a monstrous diesel pickup truck swung around the bend and slowed. The driver's side window descended, an elbow emerged, and a voice drawled at us. "What seems to be the matter here, boys?"

We thought the matter was rather clear and failed to respond.

"Ah, you got yerself a rattler!"

The door of the truck swung open and a pair of cowboy boots dangled above the road. Then the boots dropped, bearing a man with them. He stretched and his belly fell from beneath his tank top undershirt. He was wearing boxer shorts, cowboy boots, and the largest cowboy hat I have ever seen. He nodded at us and sidled casually over to the snake. The dying serpent held its defense and reared up hissing, its rattle chattering with menace.

"She is one pissed off little bitch, ain't she?" he said with his hands on his hips, as he looked down at the writhing, spitting viper. "Well, I got somthin that can take care o this."

He returned to his truck and heaved himself up into the interior. Moments later, he dropped to the ground again bearing a rifle. He walked up to the snake and stooped down to look it in the face. Wild with the surge of death, it struck at him, prepared to deal a fatal blow to any who interfered with the ending of its power. It would hold its honor to the end. The pot-bellied executioner moved his head back gently and leveled his gun. There was an earsplitting *crack* that ricocheted around the hills.

By the time I recovered from the noise, the truck was already pulling away from us.

He shouted out the window as he departed, "Make sure you bury the head so some dog don't eat it. That's where she holds her venom." He livened his vehicle with extra gas and roared out of sight.

Logan finally found his bearings and cautiously approached

the snake. It was still writhing, but only with a slow, steady, rhythmic twisting.

"Bury the head? There is no head to bury, that guy blew it clean off."

I walked up to the snake and despite the gore and the stench that rose from it, I stooped and picked her up. Instantly her muscles tightened and coiled around my hand, clenching with a surge of strength. I cried out, and tried to fling it away but could not.

"It's ok, Ben," Logan said with stern command. "It's dead, but the nerves will keep it moving for a while."

I looked at the headless serpent in the harsh glare of our headlights—an eerie form clinging to my hand. Even in death, it held the power of life.

It was still moving an hour later when we arrived back at our camp under a pregnant moon. We had hoped to eat the snake, but the stench was terrible and we figured the meat was shot. Logan skinned it however, and eventually made a belt. We tossed the body into the bushes.

"Something will make a meal of it, I hope," said Kay. "And if not, at least it's going back to the earth."

7

I sat in a corner at the tiniest of tables watching the somber astromancer trace his finger across a series of charts. I could smell mold, and was keenly aware of the presence of four or five young women lingering sad-eyed in the darkness of the decaying house, longing for the words of this aged reverend of the stars to illuminate their paths. His long, silver hair swept across the pages spread before him. Why he had asked me in to learn of my heavenly signs, I did not know. Why not the lonely women standing in the shadows near at hand? I hated the smell of the rotting house. They had told us upon our arrival that the house was abandoned because of the black mold that had invaded, yet the eerie astrologist had found it to his liking and taken up residence.

He told me a great deal about the conflicts between Aries and Cancer, my rising sign and my sun sign, and he delved into the recondite proclamations of the planets concerning my role in the transition towards the Age of Aquarius. He held me for over an hour divulging his esoteric knowledge and ended by telling me that my place of power on the planet was somewhere in the vicinity of Perth, Australia. He forced over-long eye contact of omnibus intention, and I wondered if I was supposed to rise and lead the planet to salvation.

I thanked him and walked out to the fire where the nighttime was making people weird and sad—too sad, and too silent. I wandered off into the mountain darkness to breathe fresh air and look up at the stars. They were endless, and they looked so calm, and yes, somehow wise. I guessed that many of the same stars looked down on Perth at night. Who could say what knowledge to follow through life, but out here in the wilderness, this man was regarded as a magician and the people were drawn to him. He had found his way to the mountaintop to study the cosmos away from the structured thinking of a conservative society where he was considered a quack or just full of shit. I wondered if I should go to Perth.

There was no electricity or lights on the mountain, but amplifiers had been plugged into batteries and melodies lit the night. I started to move back towards the fire.

"The sun is going to shine in my back door one day," lamented the clear voice of the Cypriot known as Watersong.

Dark shapes that eluded form gathered near the fire and

watched it lick lewdly at the sky. Those who stepped into the light were transmogrified and turned to frogs and felines.

It was the saddest party I had ever been to. I had tried to be playful with Kay and Logan, but soon we felt inappropriate and fell silent. Trying to make conversation with a pretty, pale-faced girl with a shawl draped over her head, I made light of it and asked why the mood was so somber.

"It feels like a funeral here," I confided, hoping for a bond of admission.

She looked at me with no expression. "How can one feel happy when the Earth Mother is suffering?"

I didn't have any response to this so I smiled and drifted away.

We had driven into the mountains with Brooke to "party," but mostly to lend a hand for a day on his friend's property. So we worked on the mountaintop, building frost structures to protect the plants. The nights up there were much colder than in the valley and they were desperate for hands. The work was less somber than the party.

At our meal that evening in their yurt, we chanted some *Oms* and everyone sat in respectful silence before endeavoring on a meal of marinated cucumber pasta, which was just shredded cucumber with vinegar and olive oil on it.

We were all silent until we made it down the treacherous mountain road and descended back into the warmth and life of Tipsytom.

"Do you hang out with these people, Brooke? They act like we are at the brink of the Apocalypse," Kay finally stated.

Brooke smirked. "They take life pretty seriously, I guess. Watersong and his wife, Lea, have a very spiritual relationship with the earth. I like them because they are just trying to do what they believe is right, and living with as little impact on the planet as possible."

Kay looked at him. "Sure, but do they have to be so sad? It was like a cult. Don't people have parties in order to have fun?"

Brooke sighed as if he were trying to explain a confusing subject to a child. "They are not a cult. But like-minded people get together, so all the people that work with them and hang out with them have similar values. That's why they are all out here. That's why everyone is out in these hills. They can live the way they want without someone telling them they're wrong... and yes, that community is kind of depressing."

8

We finally found the mountain lion's den. It was a well-concealed midden in the brush fifty yards from the beach, tucked up in a hard-to-reach nook at the base of the steep hill at the northern boundary of the property. The bushes were decorated with tufts of tawny hair, and there were several paw prints and some bones. We didn't hang around long, but over the next few days, we remained alert to that region of the property and finally became convinced that the mother had taken her cubs and moved on, overwhelmed by the human presence.

We tipped the scales when we arrived there. Man had won again. Our fear of the cougar turned to sadness and guilt. We had been appreciating our life in the wilds, but now we realized that with us there, it would shortly cease to be wild. I thought of the rattlesnake losing its life under the wheels of our car, and its energy in death. I thought of Watersong's farm on the mountain and the sorrowful music rippling through the quiet night.

It doesn't matter how close to nature we try to get, we are like two magnets pressed together in reverse. No matter how hard we try to reach the other, we can only push away.

Book Two

Part 2

1

We sat cross-legged in a large circle inside an enormous yurt—the ever popular yurt that graces so many marijuana farms. We were passing *energy* from one person to the next, taking a quiet moment to understand that energy, and then sharing our experience with the congregation.

"Mmmm… mmmm, wow! My energy feels like lots of little butterflies all pressed together for support and strength. Mmmm… and alone, they are so small and helpless, but together, they have sooo much strength… Yeah… here you go." The girl who had been speaking passed the energy to her neighbor who gasped.

"Whoa ho ho, that's some heavy-duty energy!" she said, wide-eyed, her heavy face contorted in an attempt to impart the might of the energy she had just received. "I'm holding the energy of the Goddess! It's the weight of peace on earth. And if I can carry that weight, then we all can!"

There was a murmur of assent as the woman lugged the energy over her lap and dumped it on her neighbor, a flimsy girl who looked bothered because *she* had hoped to feel the energy of the goddess, but wasn't certain if she was allowed to experience the same energy as another. She brightened, however, as she found a way past the dilemma.

"This is the energy of the divine feminine and it carries love for all the precious beings on Gaia." She looked relieved as she quickly unburdened herself of the divine feminine's energy in the direction of the person beside her, a grinning goon hunched forward energetically, his flat blond hair bobbing around his shoulders as he rocked back and forth caressing the energy.

"Ah, coool. Mine is like this gooey orange blob... and it's like, all warm and sticky," he said in a high nasal voice. He received a good-humored chuckle, but he wasn't done. "And it's totally full of elf magic and it wants to grow and get bigger and I think it might explode and cover us all in its happy, gooey, orange magic residue!" His hands were swelling outward as he spoke and I feared for a moment that his over-excited energy might indeed explode. "Here, take it, before it blows!" he sang out in his buzzing voice, and then heaped it onto a wide-eyed maiden who had the look of someone mortally afraid of public speaking.

It was all very nice, but I found it hard to take anyone seriously. The four speakers thus far were dressed as Little Bo Peep, a horned troll, a pixie (obviously), and Richard Nixon, although the blond fellow had his rubber mask pulled up onto his head so that he could aggressively grin at the congregation.

Brooke, Kay, Logan, and I were all dressed as pirates. We had come to the yurt party to celebrate the first birthday of twin boys whom we did not know. The mother of the twins was prevailing over this opening ceremony, seated in front of an altar covered in crystals and sprigs of cedar and incense and psychedelic paintings of light beings in coitus. She gazed around the circle with sublime tranquility. She was bare from the waist up and the two infant boys clambered around her lap suckling at her breasts. She was dark-haired and dark-skinned, her heritage probably originating from Central or South America. She had handed out the energy that was moving around the circle and she would bestow the end product of that energy on her children once it had come full circle.

Most people seemed unfamiliar with this tradition, but they were willing to give it a good effort for the sake of their new culture. Most blurted something only partially intelligible before trying to figure out how to pass on the energy, but eventually it returned to the mother for the gifting moment. When this task was accomplished and the twins steeped in sacred goddess, butterfly elf energy, and much, much more, we held a quiet moment of reverence for *Spirit,* and then quietly filed outside into the afternoon sunshine.

Brooke was full of energy. "What a great ceremony!"

Kay looked at him quizzically, his long form towering above us. "Do you think everyone is sincere? Do you think they feel the energy?"

Brooke kicked a soccer ball back to a young boy and missed his mark. It went sailing off into the middle of the pond. "Well, people have to learn that stuff. The first time, maybe someone doesn't really believe it, but then they try it and they feel something, so they give it a little more faith, and the next time they feel more." He looked shy for a moment. "I like to walk barefoot because I can feel the earth's energy."

He demonstrated that his feet were bare by digging his toes into the grass. "People in these parts are just trying to recognize these things like energy so that we don't take them for granted, or

ignore them completely. They influence us too much to be ignored."
He eyed Kay sidelong, and Kay shrugged.

"I'm just a skeptic, and I tend to think most people participate
only to conform. At least, that's why I did it."

Brooke put on his most pleasant smile. "Well that's how it
starts. Didn't you feel anything?"

"No," said Kay

"Well suit yourself, maybe you just don't want to, or you're not
tuned in enough." Brooke had the smugness of someone
dominating an argument.

"It sounds like religion the way you put it."

At this, Brooke's face drained. "No way! Maybe spiritual for
some, but it's recognizing something that is definitely there. We
can't see it; you just have to feel it... Ok, I guess that sounds like the
basis of religion, but... it's not."

Brooke seemed to lose interest but then decided that he had
parting words. "It's just teaching people to feel gratitude for what's
around them, and to get over themselves for a few minutes. That's
all."

2

We felt a bit awkward once we were out of the yurt ceremony and
turned loose on the grounds. We were at a farm and, in spite of
children playing and people milling around dressed as gorillas and
geishas, it was a place of eternal work.

The property was the Versailles of pot farms—a palace where
the outbuildings were canvas yurts and domes instead of marble-
pillared pagodas with frescoed walls. The grounds were
immaculately landscaped, with a fountain in the artificial lake.
There were grottos with carved stone statues and gravel walkways

lined with flowers and boxwood shrubs. I hadn't known that the people of that region even knew what boxwood shrubs were, especially in Lassy where trees were simply undisciplined lumber and shrubs were things that deer hid behind. But here, the square bushes were pruned and manicured, carefully placed and clearly imported. The venue was the centerfold of a *Better Homes and Gardens* magazine.

"You don't expect to see a place like this in a hippy hillbilly community," Logan said with wonder.

I shook my head in amazement. "I guess pot farmers have variation in their landscape aesthetics. Bit of a contrast to the Tipsytom cougar country, no?"

Brooke looked uncomfortable and I wasn't sure if it was the mention of cougars, or if he thought he had stumbled onto an alien planet.

We meandered around the lake where, by chance, we met the owner of the curious property. He was in his late thirties, but costumed as an old man with his hair sprayed white and a cane over which he stooped. He hobbled up and introduced himself as Joe. He seemed unable to break character.

"Howdy, young lads! How are you this fine afternoon?" His voice waivered and he clutched his lower back. "It ain't fun growin old, let me tell you."

We all chuckled, but he didn't stop. "When I was young, I used to walk ten miles through the snow to get to work and then the same going home. Uphill both ways!"

Logan chuckled again politely. "Yep, heard that once or twice."

The rest of us fell into an uncomfortable silence.

"Well, this here land you see belongs to me. Would you like to accompany an old fellow to see his garden?"

We followed him slowly towards the garden, moving at his senile pace. We learned that he was the father of the twins and that he owned Gaia, the natural food store in town. His voice broke often and he excused himself, explaining that excessive exercise at such an age made his voice falter. We remained silent, feeling terribly uncomfortable in our pirate panoply. I wondered if we should respond to him by saying, 'Ay, matey, thar be green gold on these shores, arrr!' But I resisted the urge.

We reached the garden and forgot about our guide. Brooke went limp in the knees and grabbed my shoulder for support. The ganja plants, well concealed by the crafty design of the landscape, rose up before us—neat lines of trees in rank and file, a perfect orchard. And the shock was... they were trees, the biggest ganja plants any of us had ever seen. They could have been apples or pears. They were elevated in planters and we were able to pass easily under their canopy.

"My god!" Brooke whispered beside me, still clutching my shoulder.

A pale boy with sleek dark hair to his shoulders was standing in an aisle with a clipboard. We approached, and Joe introduced us.

"Come along, young whelps, let an old fellow teach you some respect. This is my manager, Michael."

Michael looked up with clear eyes and shook our hands and greeted us with the air of someone whose job description includes being polite to visitors. He was young—maybe still a teenager.

"Why don't you show these fine gentlemen the garden facilities?" Joe pressed us forward with an encouraging nod.

There was an awkward moment when Michael took in Joe's act.

"Uh... ok," Michael said. "Do you guys want a quick tour?" he asked, snapping back to the role of a collected and ever-pleasant PR officer.

Joe shooed us off and we did our best to let the moment pass into history. We followed Michael down the grassy alleys beneath the marijuana trees.

"How much weight do you get off of these?" Brooke stammered with unreserved admiration.

"We got about ten-and-a-half-pounds from a couple last year," Michael responded promptly. "That was the first year we had the place though. I've made some improvements, so I think the majority will break nine pounds and I am hoping the Mr. Nice will hit eleven." The boy had a bit of a lisp when he talked about things that interested him.

I quietly asked Logan what was a normal harvest.

"You are stoked if you get a third of that. Each of these plants could bring in thirty to forty thousand dollars."

I gulped.

Michael slid the huge barn door open and beckoned us inside. Brooke grabbed my shoulder again, resisting the swoon that threatened to render him incapable of observing the phenomena. Michael had a veritable chemistry lab set up in the spacious outbuilding—tanks and tubes and vats and coils bubbled with strange dark liquids, and lights and panels blinked and beeped.

"We are mixing compost teas, and using a variety of nutrient mixes for some of the different regiments we run with different strains. It's all organic." Michael smiled and nodded vigorously as if this was a question always asked and he was saving us from having to bring it up.

"Well, shit. This is next level," Logan finally said because none of us could think of an appropriate question. "Whatever you are doing in here works."

Michael was unabashedly pleased by the compliment and his "thanks" had an extra lisp to it.

Brooke couldn't get over the earlier facts. "That's eleven dried pounds?"

Michael looked up pretending to think. "Yep, well, ten and a half so far." His next smile indicated that the tour was over and work was waiting.

We left the teenaged mad scientist, once again very aware of our costumes, and beat it back to the party where other birthday goers were standing in small groups looking uncomfortable. We were happy to join them.

Everyone was new in the community. The palace farm was merely in its second year and only a handful of migrant marijuana farmers who had been in the area longer than that. Many had put on a visible show of participating by donning costumes and attending the event, but once there, they were shy, and stuck to the couple of friends they recognized. It was peculiar because nobody felt entitlement; nobody had such a long history that they could put on airs of importance. There was no dominant group and nobody knew if there was somebody they should be getting to know, or if they should pretend to know how to act, or to simply smile at everyone and hope somebody would be bold enough to approach them. In the end, everyone bonded over the thing they all had in common: weed.

We ended up in a conversation with Curvy Bend (the blond-haired Nixon), and a quiet Costa Rican who worked for him. Curvy Bend bobbed his head in exaggerated fashion and told us his technique for a successful harvest was to leave the plants as long as possible regardless of weather.

"I'm just letting 'em rot, man! The more mold the better. Haha!"

I lost interest and talked to the Costa Rican who wanted to make money to support his young family, but hated California and just wanted to go home and grow orchids.

A somewhat older lesbian couple wearing camouflage and trooper helmets, and a firm-jawed cowboy joined us. One of the ladies with a shock of premature white hair explained that she had drowned, and when they brought her back from death, she had understood that she was a man in a woman's body whose mission in life was to provide medicine for people.

When we complimented the cowboy on his costume, it was revealed that he wasn't dressed up and didn't know it was a costume party. He was just a rancher who lived a few miles down the road.

On our way out, we bumped into Joe. He had removed his costume and was standing straight and plain. And his hair was brown. He shook our hands firmly.

"Thanks for coming, guys. Catch you around town," he said in a strong voice, then strode off.

3

The community of Lassy had a far more homely atmosphere than the raw lands of Tipsytom. One could see the neighbor's house, and some electricity and running water was available. It was normal to step out from the foliage of cannabis and greet neighborhood residents walking their dogs on the road. It was almost more surreal than the clandestine farm in the mountains where cougars and starvation were daily concerns. Lassy was simply a rural neighborhood where people lived mundane and unremarkable country lives, and grew marijuana instead of tulips and roses.

Kay and I hired ourselves out to one of Brooke's part-time lovers in need of farm hands. She eagerly put us to work in her garden where we toiled many long, hot, and sticky hours feeding, weeding, watering, and pruning plants. We slept in a tipi, but in reality, we lived in a pot plant for the first week.

"If people only knew the work that went into getting them high!" I exclaimed as I poured water onto my eyeballs to wash out the burning THC that had trickled in with the sweat.

"They feel it, dude, totally. Your effort makes their high that much better." Kay cursed as a twig sprang up his nose. "Just think of how much potential laughter is waiting in these plants right now. Our work is providing happiness and hilarity for multitudes of people."

A bug of some violent temperament was trying to burrow into my armpit and I squawked and flapped until I was able to extract it.

"I mean, each little bud that comes off these plants is going to provide somebody with a unique experience, maybe relief from pain. How many lives might be affected by this work? And how far will it travel? Maybe people all across the country will smoke pot from this garden and feel something positive because of it. Crazy to think about, huh?" Kay fell into a reverie, impacted by his own oratory.

I stopped inspecting my armpit and crawled deeper into the bush, trying to ignore the itchy rash that the plant matter was working deep into the skin of my forearms.

"Wow, we will be connected to so many people through this garden." Kay was suddenly in complete awe. He threw his gangly arms up into the air and grappled lovingly with the knobby boughs that rose above us and filled our lives with glowing green light. "Take for example this one lovely Romulan Haze within which we are seated. She is gonna turn into at least four pounds. That could be like... hahaha, well I have no fucking clue, but that could be individual experiences for a couple thousand people potentially, maybe more!"

I closed my eyes. All I could see were the spinning shapes of pot leaves. "Well, this plant is definitely giving me a unique experience," I said and tried to shake the images from my head. It was all I'd been dreaming about for five nights.

"Hey, Ashley!" Kay called. "You know that the president of the United States could smoke this weed? Or Michael Phelps, Or Snoop Dog?"

A brown head popped out of a nearby plant like a gnome. "Naa'aah!" she said in shrill disbelief, as if Kay had offered this tidbit as fact. "You think the President is gonna smoke Ginger's weed?"

Kay chortled. "Thousands of people are going to smoke this stuff, Ash! Tens of thousands!"

Ashley peered through the vegetation with a concerned look, as though this information bore some great influence on her life. "But if thousands of people are going to smoke it... Oh, Goddess! I can't put enough positive energy into each plant for thousands of people. What if it isn't good enough? C'mon guys, we have to try to put all of our love into each plant at every moment." She looked distressed.

Kay beamed back at her with comic delight.

Ashley raised her pitch for emphasis, but failed because her voice was always shrill and airy. "I'm serious, guys. This is a super-serious thing."

Ashley wore a perpetual look of uncertainty and frustration framed by rope-like dreadlocks. Her heavy horizontal eyebrows and baggy hemp clothing made her appear shorter than she was, and like so many canine lovers, she had grown to resemble her Australian shepherd. Ashley was Ginger's slave. She was technically a volunteer, but in fact, she was a slave. She donated her energy and work to the farm until there was weed to trim because she carried the guilt of the world on her shoulders and felt as if she was taking advantage of those who needed help by asking for money. This had fit conveniently into Ginger's personal brand of tyranny and Ashley had taken up her assigned role as an underachieving, ungrateful servant. Believing her unworthiness to be a truth, Ashley denounced her ineptness on a daily basis. Ginger gently encouraged this sentiment with nods of understanding, nice words of affirmation, and a benign twinkle in her eye.

4

Ginger was a smiling despot with a penchant for manipulation and a body that grew daily. She had welcomed us with generous and open arms, and for the first three days, cooked ample and astonishing feasts in her outdoor kitchen situated mid-way up Balsam Hill on a dirt track just outside of Lassy. Her whole house was outdoors, but she pretended it was a palace. She slept in a pavilion with fur rugs and satin drapes in a king-sized four-poster bed.

"I'm a witch, you see. When the storms come, it won't rain here." She looked at us with the smile of an imp. "I'm also a queen of the fairies. Be careful, because my seductions are not intentional, but many fall for my spell."

I had an uncomfortable feeling that she was being sincere.

"Yeah, I noticed the streak of royalty. You have your toilet on a dais with velvet curtains around it," said Kay with a lovable laugh. "I thought it was a throne at first."

She gave him a half-smile, which admonished him and told him that coarse humor was for plebeians, not Fairy Queens.

Neither Kay nor I were unintentionally seduced despite Ginger's unintentional promenading and unintentional coquettish smiles, and the shy twirling of her blonde curls around her chubby fingers. And, after three days, the glorious meals vanished and the weather grew inexplicably colder at night. Ginger watched us as her body expanded and the thunderheads built in her mind and she conceived ways to destroy us.

"She has a thyroid problem," said Roger. "And she's a crazy bitch," he added.

We were at the base of Balsam Hill with the French Canadians and Floridians, drinking cold beers and waiting for Michael. Roger, graying and ambitious, had quit Quebec with the goal of turning his modest retirement funds from his career as a grade school teacher into a fortune, and had brought his nephews, Anton and Jean, along to help. "I really didn't think it was humanly possible for a person to gain weight that quickly! At first she worked hard, but now she just complains and pities herself and expects others to do the work for her!" Roger had a special hatred for Ginger and it seemed to grow the more she did.

Jean was trotting out a very French-sounding tune on his guitar. "Forget her, Roger, there's plenty more to worry about here."

Jean's statement was completely untrue. Although this grow operation didn't have the tidy manicured look of Joe's farm, and it was not as extensive, it was one of the best-prepared farms I had seen. For one thing, they were connected to the grid and were the source of all electrical power for Balsam Hill. Being at the bottom of the three lots, they had ample flat ground, which allowed them to use tractors and other heavy machinery to dig, relocate heavy objects, and load vehicles. Their watering and feeding system was regulated and precise, and run out of a garage they could drive into with the massive bags and drums of nutrients. They had one house dedicated to cloning plants and germinating seeds, and a sophisticated dry-room with sliding racks, fans, vents, and dehumidifiers, so they could control the temperature. They had nothing to worry about, and so spent the afternoons drinking beer and playing basketball in the driveway. Roger was bored, and hating Ginger gave him something to do.

Bobby was restless and bored with waiting. He was climbing a tree with graceful, controlled movements. He leapt, and caught a branch well above his standing reach and pulled himself up with ease. The tight bands of muscles in his torso were too numerous to count—whole groups of fiber unknown to me. Bobby was a rock climber first and a weed farmer second, and irritated because he was hoping to get out for an afternoon climb after the consultation with Michael, who was late.

Bobby and his friend, Ivory, were the energetic Floridians who managed the third plot of land near the top of the hill, an area we called "The Tower." Their infrastructure was based on Roger's operation, and Bobby regularly ran past our curtilage on his way down to Roger's, and then back up to the top of the hill. He was always running.

Michael eventually arrived and Bobby emerged from the thicket of leaves. Michael had the air of a country doctor who makes house calls and is universally loved. We crowded around him as he silently inspected the plants. Then he snapped out a pocket-sized microscope to carefully inspect the buds. I thought he might produce a stethoscope and listen to the plant's heartbeats, but he had his diagnosis and in this case, the stethoscope was unnecessary.

"What's your ratio of phosphorus to water?" Michael asked Roger, as if he were a stern, yet kindly, practitioner.

Roger looked at Anton. "Sixteen parts," was the reply.

"Ok, you should drop it to twelve percent for the next cycle. Six day cycle, I guess?" he lisped.

Anton nodded.

"It's not precise. Just finish this cycle as you have it, and drop it to twelve for the second one. You can keep the nitrogen and potassium content as it is. I think this OG Kush will be ready in about three weeks, so after one more full nutrient cycle cut out everything except magnesium for three days before you do the pure water flush."

Anton nodded again.

We moved on to another strain and Michael performed another physical.

"The Blue Dream looks great. Everyone is having a good year with them. But if I were you, I would choose one for an early harvest, even next week. Here, take a look at those crystals. See how clear they are? They are mature but they haven't clouded up yet. That means you are going to have a much lighter clearer high. If they get cloudy, the effect in your head will be heavier. Early harvest is nice with the Blue Dream because it's such a psychoactive strain already."

5

Lassy had the usual ungainliness of a boomtown—a weary and forgotten place preparing for a peaceful decline, surprised when it suddenly becomes a bustling metropolis. And while rushing to see to the needs of its new guests, it forgot to dress.

There was one road through the town, and for most travelers that was enough to convince them to pass through without stopping, although visitors were rare because there was no place to pass through to—only grave errors of map interpretation led people to accidently find Lassy.

I was in the laundromat one day cleaning the familiar smelling green detritus from the lint trap so that my own clothes could refill it with the same matter, when I noticed a grizzled gray-haired man with bones dangling from his ears watching me. I knew instantly he was a pot farmer because fashion in those remote areas was a badge of occupation. Stereotypes aside, I had not met anyone with dreadlocks and hemp clothing who was not in the ganja trade.

When he caught my eye, he approached and spoke in a low voice. There was no preamble.

"It is of great importance that you always remember ganja is sacred. It is a medicine for all people." His eyes were too white, his voice so gruff that it was gentle, and I was distracted by the odor of his breath. But I didn't stop him from conveying his message.

"I see all of you young people coming to Lassy to make money, but we aren't here for money. We have to remember that we are here for the spiritual health of the world. That's why we can't bastardize the plant! It can't just be about the money!"

I opened my mouth to offer my views, but he stopped me.

"I don't accuse you; I say this to remind you, and so that you will remind your friends, because you are young and people have to learn. You have to share it and teach it. The plant can't be forgotten. I have been growing ganja for thirty-three years in California, and I never forget that the plant is sacred. I'm afraid people will forget the plant is a gift from the earth and that it heals. And I am afraid it will become the object of greed. So I teach." His voice dropped lower. "Do you understand? The plant is medicine. It is sacred. And there are hundreds of new, young folk showing up every day, and they don't know."

I returned his gaze and tried to smile. "I guess there are more people here to learn about it then. I'll remember."

He looked at me unblinking for a few moments and then took a deep breath and put his hand on my heart. Then he returned to folding his clothes. I started my laundry and fled into the daylight to stare at the soft curves of the hills that ringed the valley.

I looked at the street. There were far more people than one would imagine in a town that small. Colorful people who, even if you couldn't place them by their clothing, looked as though they came from elsewhere. All of them fit in, because none of them did.

At that moment, I recognized that something bigger was happening than what I had imagined. My image of a private, little subculture in the hills was giving way to a much more impactful human event, a much bigger subculture with a far more expansive effect. It was a scene I had fallen into in my naïve enthusiasm for a different manner of living. It was a scene that many were now stumbling into and certainly, it had been growing and strengthening for far longer than I knew. But now it was exploding. This startled little backwater town—turned metropolis—said it clearly.

Everything about Lassy was confusing because when the new comes, the old does not simply pack up and move away.

The road through town was a face-off. There was the tavern with the slouching stairs and cigarette smoke billowing from the front door whenever it opened, where men in cowboy boots and clean faces stood on the porch and looked across the road at the recently opened café with the hand-painted sign of peaceful trees and its traffic of strangely clad youth. The grocery that had supplied the town with soda and frozen food for the last thirty years, and illuminated their shopping space with florescent lights, stared gloomily over at the tiny store with Tibetan prayer flags in the window that sold no soda or frozen foods, had prices four times higher, yet somehow had twice as many patrons. The Yoga studio was shoulder-to-shoulder with the dime store, and they were both bewildered by the other's existence. The mercantile shop thought itself clever and was advertising tie-dyed shirts in the window.

I left my wash and headed for the Yoga studio in search of a girl I had taken an interest in. When I looked up and down the street, I could see the full picture—these outlandish new venues stood out from the normal elements of the town and had clustered together for support because they were so out of place in Lassy. The gas station, the mechanic, the hardware store, the BBQ joint and the Mexican restaurant all looked settled and at home. On the surface, the old era of the town was still dominant, but when I looked at the people on the street, it seemed as though the original inhabitants were rapidly becoming a minority.

It was all a visual contrast more than a practical one, and I didn't like to think of the old and the new as being in conflict, or even so very separate. Though Capricorn Café and Gaia Natural Foods were important social centers, the newly arrived relied on the existence of the old town, and it was foolish to believe that the immigrants did not dart into the old grocery for their basics, or swing by the tavern to meet some of the valley's old land barons and to drink a whiskey.

Still, it was fine entertainment to sit at the gas station and watch the cars come and go. The activity at the pumps told the story of the social collision better than anywhere else.

A tired mother with a car of unruly children en route to school might share a moment at a pump with a car too small and dilapidated for the mountain roads to Lassy, full of tattooed punks wearing spiked collars, shredded jeans, and vests with patches advertising anarchy. The children gape as the guy with the pink Mohawk tries to figure out how the gas pump works.

The thick-bellied reverend, who keeps a uniform and

predictable flock, eyes the neighboring car uncertainly as he scrubs his windshield, trying to force the notion into his mind that the boy with the earrings and the pristine hair might be wearing a woman's blouse, and that the pretty one holding his hand might also be a boy.

The barrel-chested logger with burly forearms and absolute confidence in his masculinity hops from his Ford F350, brushes brush off his Carhart jeans and flannel shirt, stomps the mud from his Wolverine boots, then heads towards the mini-market. He nods at the identical Ford F350 that pulls in and then does a double take when a dreadlocked woman wearing Carhart jeans, Wolverine boots, and a flannel shirt hops out and casually lifts a hundred-and-fifty-pound generator from the bed of her truck.

The conservative man with the horse trailer who likes hard workers whoever they are, but not bums, keeps a suspicious eye on the grimy, bearded man with no teeth standing outside the gas station market, because in these strange times he doesn't know if he is observing a hard worker or a bum.

The teenage girl, waiting her whole life to escape from Lassy and planning to leave for college the next week, stares as four golden chariots, each bearing three strapping, untamed Adonises, all unclaimed and virile, pulls into town. She spends the next five hours crying in her car and then returns home to tell her parents she doesn't want to go to college after all, and will trim weed instead.

As I made my way to the Yoga studio, I thought of the preacher in the laundromat and wondered how many of the immigrants held the opinion that marijuana was a sacred medicine. How many of the old-timers thought of the plant that way? I was certain that among both groups money was a large consideration. I looked one more time at the awkward new beginnings of an old

and battered town, and wondered if maybe the gift of the ɪ
not what it could do for individuals, but what it could for societies.

6

Though she stood by her dictate that the rain would not fall on her
queendom, Ginger decided an upgrade was in order. The only
structure on Balsam Hill was a retired goat shed, so it was there that
she laid plans for her new palace. It was necessary to fight a
number of battles since the building was already claimed—several
colonies of wasps controlled territory under the eaves, and the
snakes and lizards and scorpions ruled the underworld beneath the
disintegrating floor. The anarchic kingdom of the rats dominated all
parts between.

Ashley watched us with disapproval when we touched fire to a
coffee tin full of moss and positioned the smoking can beneath one
of the wasp's papery globes.

"They didn't do anything to you," she said miserably.

"Yes, but they certainly will," replied Kay. "Besides, they have a
vacation home at Roger's where they go on weekends. They will
probably just move there permanently."

Ashley's eyes widened as she pondered and watched the
enraged wasps. "Naa'aah," she finally opined with amused
suspicion.

Kay sighed. "You're right, that's a lie, but we figured we would
give them a chance. Ginger said if they aren't out by tomorrow
morning, we have to kill them. But in that case, you can use the nest
as parchment!"

Ashley had a devoted interest in earth-based products, and we
knew how to entice her.

"Really? Do you think I could make a book with the nest?"

Kay nodded, "You just need some string to bind it."

Ashley was annoyed by this. "Using string defeats the purpose of a wild-crafted book. Maybe I could use some animal sinew or something to bind it. There were some guys at the last Rainbow Gathering who used sinew to stitch clothing. Yeah! That's what I'll do."

A wasp looped by and I wondered if our safe distance could be extended. "You might have to kill an animal if you want to make sinew," I said.

Ashley looked at me with repugnance and disgust. "Spirit says it is wrong to kill animals."

Kay sniggered and Ashley's hurt expression cracked into a shy smile. "Well it's truuue!" she defended, her voice shrill and emotive. She didn't understand why we found her philosophical statements comical, but our amusement was amusing to her. She started to giggle.

"Well, you can use road kill," I said, and she brightened at the possibility.

"But if you want to do it right, you will have to make all the tools used to make the book." Kay was grave.

Ashley's laughter trailed off. "Oh, I didn't think about that... Well, I probably need a knife. Maybe I could find a sharp stone. I could make the handle from wood...."

"You need a paper press," Kay added. "Those are usually metal."

Ashley became even more flustered. "Do I need to learn how to use a forge?"

Kay nodded, "Yeah, and to mine the ore. And you need to turn the nest into paper too, which probably requires glue."

She looked at him, her despair expanding. "How do I make natural glue?"

Kay smiled a victorious and wicked smile. "Probably you'll have to boil a horse. You can use the donkey across the street that wakes me up every morning."

Ashley groaned, "But spirit says I can't kill animals... I guess I don't need a book." She looked down at her loyal canine friend who had been watching the wasps with concern. "We don't need a wasp-paper book, do we, River Otter Heart Heron?" The dog looked up at the sound of its name and licked her hand lovingly. "I didn't think so!"

Part of marijuana farming *does* necessitate that you do everything on your own. It was generally taboo to call in a professional plumber or electrician who might take umbrage to the growing of cannabis and report you, so self-sufficiency was part of the occupation. We spent two days shoveling rotten hay and rat excrement from the miasmic gloom of the goat shed's inner chamber. We added a water line to the main up the hill, and piped it through the shed wall. We sprayed everything with water, then scraped the walls and hung heavy plastic sheeting. We built a counter and put in a sink, and installed a woodstove, refrigerator, and a propane stove. Then we heaved all of Ginger's belongings down the hill and she crept in with dainty, cautious steps to inspect our work. Finding it displeasing, but deciding to take up residence anyway, she banished us to the woods to dig a new latrine while she hung her tapestries and laid her rugs.

We spent the next days in the annex of the shed, setting up a dry room for the plants, building racks, running power lines from Roger's place, and installing outlets for the fans and dehumidifiers. And just when we were considering mutiny, Bobby and Ivory showed up and reminded us that there was a world outside of the shit-filled goat shed.

We all hopped in a car with the French Canadians and roared through town to a rendezvous at the local grocery. There were several trucks full of energetic youth committing the crime of truancy from their farm work. The afternoon was perfect. I wondered if Lassy had ever hosted this many twenty-somethings at one time. There were at least forty of us, and we were from all over the country and beyond, and we had all converged on the tiny backcountry town of Lassy, California, because that was where we had the freedom to explore new lifestyles without the pressures of society. And we could earn a living at the same time.

7

The California Green Rush was sparked by an economic opportunity. The legal loopholes and the demand for the product allowed for the rapid expansion of an industry. And with the offer of cash with no strings attached, the people came. But the influx of seasonal workers brought with them something else on their quest for money—an undercurrent of protest and a desire to live their personal forms of freedom. The opportunity for economic gain mobilized an undefined, yet powerful movement of peoples. And by leaving their parent culture, this wholly diverse and varied group of individuals arrived with a common goal. A fledgling culture began to take shape.

This new culture was defined less by customs, material items, or social structure than by the opportunity for liberty. It is a culture of silent protest. It never represented any particular group that needed to stand up and defend themselves. It is not an outward surge of objection, a blossoming of defiance and anger towards oppression. It is not a loud cry for change—unlike the civil rights movement of the 1960s where the people gathered to show their strength. This new culture developed in between the folds of another great and powerful culture, hoping only to find its own place and to develop optimistic ideals for the future of civilization — to reestablish freedom. It is the new face of the American Dream.

The annual migration to California has been a subtle affair. There was never a public offer of work in the great marijuana plantations of the west. There were no extensive caravans pouring in to settle huge tracts of untamed lands. It developed through quiet action. It is a movement spread by word of mouth, and through one human interaction at a time. The movement found the people it suited. Those who feel a call of self-determination slowly trickle in, but they don't abandon their old existences or leave them behind forever because they are joining a movement that does not intend to separate from society, but to grow among it and to gently, non-intrusively, spread its ideals.

It is a clever culture, asking so little of its members. To participate, and to be present for a time, is enough. As a community made of seasonal workers, the strength of the culture is in its elasticity and migratory nature—seasonal work necessitates that the culture's participants disperse and return to their homes, or travel elsewhere, spreading ideas and stories like seeds. The diversity of the individuals in the culture allows ideas and the values it nurtures to percolate throughout society so that those notions begin to feel normal. By traveling, the culture finds other pockets of common ideology and compliments them with new energy, naturally integrating, and what at one moment appears to be a radical subculture, suddenly begins to seem like a common and accepted way of life throughout society. It is a culture of protest. It is a culture of silent action.

Of course, then as now, not all participants (including myself) understood what we were a part of, and sometimes an unobtrusive culture must let its members stumble along, bickering and debating. That time in California represented many things for many people. For some it was about money. For others, love of a plant. And for the rest, it was the opportunity to explore new lifestyles and live their own values. The plant provided an environment and opportunity for something new.

The stories I listened to led me to believe that I had found a way to practice liberty at a time when many citizens of the United States, and elsewhere, felt as if their choice of lifestyle was stifled or not possible within the expectations and regulations of the societal milieu. We were a fringe movement looking for a way forward, and we broke rules and constraints—the American dream always has.

8

We drove for a couple of hours out to a ravine scored into the earth by time and the elements. We explored the endless and perfidious caves and watched Bobby and the other adept climbers crawl like spiders across the cliff faces. The sun slanted into the gorge and it seemed like a world that knew no unhappiness.

Reality is that the indigenous community living in a village to the east had been massacred by the angry settlers of the Gold Rush following some vague and unrecorded disagreement. The surviving members of the community fled into the caves for refuge, and so the immigrants dynamited the openings and entombed the retreating victims.

Anton's face was grim as he told this story on that calm, sunny afternoon. "By searching for our own independence, we became invaders. We should be sensitive to the ways of those who came before us."

His brother, Jean, shrugged under the weight of irony, "Those whose lands we are invading were the invaders before us, a chain that goes on and on. There is no place without peoples," he said in his rich French accent. "So live your way, but choose a good and non-intrusive way with the peoples around you."

When we returned to the goat shed, Ginger was livid. "I didn't say you could leave! You act as if you are free to come and go! But I am a dragon woman, and you can't walk over me!"

Ginger bellowed, then stomped around the shed with her nose flared. "I open my home to you!" She spread her hands to impress on us the decaying goat shed we had remodeled, "and you show me no gratitude! But my manager is coming tomorrow. He won't accept your behavior. He will demand respect... Oh, and he will stay in the tipi, so you need to find somewhere else to sleep after tomorrow."

We wandered off into the dark wondering exactly what a "dragon woman" was, and wondering if we should be concerned. And more importantly, who was this new dictator? By the sound of it, a real menace.

"God-damn," said Kay with a sigh. "Still, it's the money that wins the argument. I'd be out of here in a flash if I didn't need those dollars."

I nodded to the darkness. "Yep, we can escape a lot, but not that just yet."

9

He was gentle as a lamb, happy as a clam, and goofy as a goat. Our new manager didn't particularly believe in management. He was more interested in meditation, making silly rhymes, and cooking Indian food.

Rubicon was from the Bronx, but had spent most of the last few years in various Ashrams in India. He had a large, lopsided head that was constantly adjusting its shape and forming new lumps. His face was broad, his nose small, and his eyes just a little lazy.

The first night he cooked Indian food for us. And Ginger, insulted that she had to share her kitchen, went to the BBQ joint in town.

"What's up with this environ, my weird, wacky, wending wayfarers? It's like the depression bombs have been dropping around here." His voice popped and jabbed with street spark.

We were all on quests of varying success to control our egos and not slander others, so none of us wanted to share our opinion of Ginger. His large crystalline eyes watched us with shrewd understanding.

"She has got some demon screamin in her head maybe? It's cool though, you folks feel the love movement! YEAH! SILENCE THE VIOLENCE!" Rubicon mandated, and gently touched his palm to his forehead.

It turned out Rubicon had never met Ginger before; his connection was through a mutual acquaintance. Nor had he ever worked with weed and had almost no interest in the plant. Nor had he ever held a managerial job. He just liked to cook Indian food.

"Yo, Ashley, get in on some o this fiiine ayurvedic cuisine."

Ashley looked longingly at the aromatic piles of food and sighed dejectedly. "Spirit says I should eat only raw food."

Ashley of late had indeed given up cooked food and was subsisting on kale, which fortunately, she fervently loved. Now she was chewing her leaves and some assorted seeds.

"That's right, Spirit knows best!" Rubicon concurred. "Tuck in, breth-rin!"

Ashley looked glum as we ate. "Well, River Otter is eating raw foods with me because he understands."

River Otter Heart Heron was sitting by the door looking distinctly pallid for an Australian Shepherd. He stared at our mouths as we filled them with food.

"Yeah, I can see how River Otter would be a raw foodist," said Kay, "though he might include some meat in his raw routine."

Ashley scowled and tossed her dog some kale. "I know, dogs need meat, but it's just so hard to know how to do the right thing. If he is going to eat meat, then I think I should hunt it myself."

Rubicon had folded his legs beneath him on the stool, pressed his palms together in front of his chest, and begun praying. We held our breaths. A moment later his eyes popped open and a huge smile sprang to his face.

"All is good. I just spoke with Spirit. The word on the street is that the dog gets to eat! Taking care of the body comes first. The rest will follow!"

Ashley looked deeply relieved, "Reeaally?" she couldn't suppress a smile, and from then on she understood Rubicon to be a divine channel.

10

Ginger felt betrayed and she began to make voodoo dolls in our likeness, and to spy on us from the goat shed. We would move around the garden, preparing for the harvest, and try to ignore her blonde head darting out of sight every time we glanced down the hill towards her shed.

"You didn't whip us into shape, Rube," Kay explained. "Didn't you know that is what you are here for?"

Kay and I were generally lighthearted, but Rubicon took the situation seriously once he had observed for a few days. There had been some tense conversations, and the urban monk was pensive.

One day he sat up (he refused to let us move from the tipi and so the three of us shared it) and declared that he was taking a vow of silence for twenty-four hours. "Sometimes your tongue must stay still so that your mind can work." And having said those words, we didn't hear a sound from him until the following morning.

It so happened that the day on which Rubicon took his vow of silence, we had business in town. Kay, Ashley, and I dragged him along to buy dog food and other supplies and he sat outside Gaia Natural Foods with benign grace, staring into the ether.

When we came out, he was being interviewed by a reporter from the *Los Angeles Times*, in town to get the story on the workings of the illegal marijuana industry. Rubicon had been the reporter's first likely candidate as he was clearly sitting around with nothing to do. Rubicon had somehow communicated his commitment to silence and was listening carefully to the reporter's questions, then writing down his answers on a napkin, emphasizing his intent with his palms pressed together and a great deal of bowing.

On Sunday, we found a copy of the paper. Rube had made the second page, and the article largely condemned our community's influence on the area, opining that the weed industry had brought crime, drugs, and disrespect to a quiet and content town that wanted nothing to do with marijuana. The article interviewed residents who lamented the rapid changes: unsavory and dangerous new neighbors, their own youth now smoking cannabis, and property prices on the rise. Rubicon was un-phased.

"Yeah, my fellahs," he cried in delight, "I told her we were all blessed peoples, me and her and all of us! Well, she didn't write that part, she mostly said I was eating ice cream, but we all get the message!" He looked up at the sky and lifted his arms. "Don't think twice about Ginger. She just wants to be loved like everyone else. People come to a place like this because they think it's easier to find the love here. They don't know that it is everywhere. She will learn. Be at peace. Be at peace." Rubicon bowed his head and pressed his palms together.

11

Even though there were no stoplights, and two people could stand at opposite ends of the town and hold a conversation with hardly a raised voice, the immigrant population treated Lassy like an urban center. Events were hosted nearly every day. Invitations were open to anyone, but mostly it was the weed-growing community that attended. Our favorite event was the weekly ecstatic dance, a lively romp held in the backyard of Gaia. I was unclear on the principles of ecstatic dance until my first experience—during which I learned that one's body does anything and everything it wants to. Admittedly, I was more of a voyeur than a participant, and often sat on the sideline drinking Kombucha tea and watching my acquaintances spasm to the electronic music.

One wonderful trademark of the farming community was that age was not considered when developing friendships. Rubicon and I struck up an active friendship with a couple of six-year-old hoodlums named Orion and Lavender who had a penchant for disobeying whenever their mothers were spinning and jerking wildly in the dance. Rubicon and I abetted them during some of their more unforgivable crimes such as stuffing pinecones into the cast-off shoes of unsuspecting dancers, and erasing the better part of the letters on the white board in front of the store, so that instead of reading *Dance Tuesday—Mobilize Your Body,* it said, *DuMBo.*

During one such ecstatic event, a homeless man became intrigued by the commotion and wandered onto the grass swaying and smiling and smelling of spirits. He noticed Lavender pulling at the ears of a dog and offered her a dance. The world transitioned in seconds from swaying lashing bodies moving to organic sounds to a silent ring of fearful-eyed onlookers.

"Um, sir, can I help you? Did you lose your way? This is my daughter."

Rubicon walked out of the store, and without a second glance walked up to the circle. "What's good, my brotha?" he said to the homeless man. "Can I give you a ride somewhere?"

The weatherworn roadman, disoriented by the change of mood, looked around in confusion searching for where that voice came from, and then latching on to the one smiling face, was drawn to the invitation. Since Rubicon didn't have a car, it was more accurately me who would do the driving. So we took him down to the river where he had a camp.

On the drive back, Rube was in one of his rare serious moods. "There is always fear of the outsider. You form a community of outsiders, but when you come together, the rules have already been written because the community boundaries are the common ideals, not the individual's ideals. We are outsiders to some because they fear us. And because they fear us, we remain outsiders. Our friend, who lives by the creek, is an outsider because he is feared, and due to that fear, he will remain an outsider. It's an eternal cycle."

We drove on down to the grocery store for more affordable food than what was offered at Gaia, and when we returned to the car, a frumpy lady caught our attention. She addressed us with caustic words.

"You know what? Guys like you are destroying this community! You think you can come in here and do what you want. I caught my twelve-year-old son with pot last week. A few years ago, the kids didn't know that stuff existed. We would be happy if ya'll packed your bags and went back to whatever evil place you came from!"

I was shocked because most of my interactions with the Lassy residents had been cordial. We drove on in silence and when we reached our venue the elated dancers were gathered in a circle singing, "Earth my body, water my spirit." Lavender and Orion were trying to fasten a cardboard saddle to a patient border collie.

"Are we destroying their community, Rube?"

He was swaying to the sounds of the singing. "Well, we're changing it. I don't know if it's good or bad, but we're changing it."

12

Buzzwords rang in my ears: sacred, ceremony, medicine, manifest, healing, spirit, goddess, holding space, divine feminine, family, being present, synchronicity, speaking your truth.

I was hearing the words so frequently that they wanted to pour from my lips uncontrolled. I wondered when someone would ask me if I was having a good day and I would reply, "Being present, thank you!" or I would be on the toilet and someone would knock and I would blurt out, "I'm manifesting, give me a sec." I was starting to wonder if every event was a "ceremony," and if all food and drink were now classed as good or bad "medicine." Those who'd had an argument, or heard derogatory remarks, or had been born into our tumultuous world, had a great deal of "healing" to accomplish. A walk in nature could be "sacred," as was a pretty stone, and sometimes intercourse—if it was performed appropriately. Even a good party or a handmade spoon had the capacity for sacredness, and of course anyone of the female gender was automatically "sacred," and also a "goddess," and also the "divine feminine." Your "family" could be a blood relation, it might also be a friend, it might be those with whom you attend a ceremony, or it might be the whole community, or even the entire population of the world along with "spirit." To "speak one's truth" was simply to say whatever you were feeling, but whenever one needed to emphasize an opinion, they would severely state that they were "speaking their truth." Coincidental moments, or unexpected occurrences, or meeting someone and deciding that you liked them, or things just going your way in general was attributed to "synchronicity." Any time someone experienced emotional hardship and was suffering, or hopefully "healing," those in the vicinity had the obligation of "holding space" for the challenged individual.

It seemed like a nice term for waiting around and making yourself available, so I tried it one day when sitting in the car outside Gaia waiting for Kay and Rubicon and Ashley. Curvy Bend saw me and asked what was happening.

"Just holding space for Kay and Rube and Ash."

Curvy nodded. "Ah coool, man, thanks for speaking your truth, brother."

On another occasion, at the hardware store while the keeper was in back looking for some parts I had requested, I saw Joe.

"Wow! What synchronicity to see you here! What are you doing these days?" he asked politely.

"Oh," I responded casually. "Just holding space."

He looked confused. "At Ginger's place?"

"Well, yes, there too, but just now while I wait for some hardware."

He allowed the sacred knowledge to sink in and concentrated on attaining it, then patted me on the shoulder. "Everything is gonna work out, just be present and keep holding space and you will manifest what you need."

And lo! I manifested the bolts I was looking for.

The next day, Ginger told me to carry a bag of fertilizer up to the Tower lot for Bobby. I wrapped my arms around the air in front of me.

"I don't think I can, Ginger. I'm holding space."

She glared at me and prodded my voodoo avatar with a needle. I stopped holding space and held the fertilizer instead.

I was grooming the plants with Rubicon as we discussed the subject with some vehemence.

"That's not cool school you feel?" Rube rapped, "You gotta treat the words themselves like they are *sacred!*"

His face expanded into an amphibious smile and his head bulged in several new places at his clever joke. "But seriously, those are powerful words, and they get weak if they aren't used to their full potential, like if they are wasted in some wack situation." He looked perplexed. "I mean, what next? Folks gonna fling curses with these sacred utterances? Goddess, dammit! You divine feminine BITCH!" He stopped and stared at me, waiting for my response.

I shot him a look that said I heard him but didn't have a response.

"Yeeah," he said. "Don't mind my divine wisdom! Keep giving that green goddess all yo love!" He broke into a fit of laughter at his own wit and nearly impaled himself with the pruners. The strain of weed we were working with was, in fact, called Green Goddess, although I'd heard that the variety had originally been known as Green Crack.

"But at the same time, they are just words, and words can be recycled," I said. "Tons of words have multiple meanings and are always changing to suit new situations. Words form the vernacular of a developing culture and they help people identify with one another, and also create identity. It's speech accommodation; language convergence. It helps people feel like they belong. The words might get old, but I think the people using them are mostly genuine, or at least trying to fit in, which isn't a bad thing."

Rubicon stared at me as if I were an alien. His face was pulled into an expression of extreme disbelief. Personally, I thought *he* looked like an alien.

"Wawawawaa? So you can just appropriate whatever word you want and make it your own? All right, from now on, when I say 'I love you,' it really means 'I think you smell funky.'"

I rolled my eyes. "But people around here believe in the things these words represent and they are trying to embody them. Yeah, they are a little over-emphatic sometimes, or they get preachy, or the ego gets a little too much of a grip, but the words remind you of how you want to live."

Kay trotted by on his way to the goat shed and Rubicon yelled loudly, "I love you, Kay! You family!" and winked at me.

"I can't talk," Kay responded. "I have to manifest a handsaw. The guys are harvesting some medicine up at The Tower and I'm gonna hold space for them. If we get through it fast, we can make it to the sacred healing ceremony in town with family!" He loped off.

"Oh goddess!" I muttered under my breath.

13

Ginger hosted a woman's gathering in the goat shed, and only grudgingly allowed me to remain in the vicinity, reminding me to stay invisible. Even in a realm where freedom is making an admirable comeback, there are those who abuse their power. Unfortunately, when you live where you work, an employer can forget that their employees are not available for their needs at all times. Kay had left, so had Rubicon, and finally Ashley, too. Ashley found her dream job growing kale somewhere near the coast, possibly the only thing that would have convinced her to risk the curses and black spells that Ginger unleashed on her for the abandonment. Then it was just me.

I hung out with Lavender and Orion, trying to catch mice while it was still light, but once the sun went down, there was nothing to do but loiter by the shed. The twins and their mother, Roshan, were there, and she was talking about polyamory. It turned out that Joe was interested in open relationships.

"I believe in the freedom of love," she said delicately, "but I don't know if Joe understands it the right way."

I knew the prevailing stereotype of male pot farm owners and their tendency to hire small armies of attractive young women. Trimming was a desirable job, and the rugged mountain men that had their own operations often took full advantage of this to meet females. It was, in fact, how Roshan had met Joe, and the result had been twins. Through Roshan's polite suggestions, she expressed that Joe was not interested in giving up his carefree trim-scene lifestyle, and that she was conflicted about his values.

I watched the group of women talking and wondered where they had all been a couple of years before—what they had been doing, who they had been. People in those parts carried their histories like hidden wedding rings. Many were trying out a new lifestyle, and history was just a chain that held them back. In some respects, it was *because* nobody had a history that the culture and personality of a community developed so quickly. The blank-book people adopted appealing traits, and fleshed out their characters. They tried out new ideas in spirituality and diet and sexuality, and learned new life skills and living environments. Of course, many came as they were and stayed so, but the nature of the young culture allowed those looking for something new to easily become *it*.

I was reminded that the way we all looked said nothing of what we had come from. A vibrant, rosy-cheeked, free spirit with dreadlocks, wearing handmade clothing, who practiced tantric yoga and lived on a vegan commune, might, only months before, have been dressed in name-brand clothes and grabbed a McDonald's burger as she dashed to work in the strip mall.

And if the act didn't suit them? Would these young multitudes that were looking for something different just pick up and leave? Certainly! Many did. If you were not dedicated to a remote, back-to-the-land lifestyle or communal living, or didn't enjoy the work, or simply didn't have the right resources to make it a permanent existence, or simply didn't like what you were part of, you could leave and take the lessons with you and abandon the character you had created. You could forget the culture you had so carelessly and casually joined. It was a culture of temporary participants held together by supply and demand. I wondered if it was a nationwide youth trend. Everyone wanted to explore and dabble in multiform lifestyles, and everyone wanted an easy escape too. It was part of searching for individuality and for a pathway into a more promising future.

I wondered if Roshan would decide one day that she didn't believe in polyamory, take her boys, and leave the valley. What would come next? Would the values remain? Or was it a casual experiment? Just a lifestyle to live for a time? Maybe she would be a waitress some day, or a secretary in a neat suit instead of a colorful flowing dress. Maybe she would go back to school and work for science, or the government.

Her babies fumbled and fussed on her lap—the next

generation. Would they stay and develop with the culture and grow up to represent it? Would they be the ones who would make it permanent? Or would it change too quickly, before they had a chance to understand what they had come from? The babies and the culture were in a nascent phase of existence, and both had an unknown and moldable future.

I felt worn out. I caught my reflection in a full-body mirror and wondered what people imagined me to be. I wondered how different I seemed in this place from what I had been and what I would be. I looked like shit. I was coated in resin and had a permanent, aggressive odor of ganja about me. My clothing was filthy and I was increasingly bearded. It was just easier in the conditions in which we worked and lived to be that way. I could see where the stereotypes arose.

Two days later, after securing the farm on Balsam Hill, I went to ask Roger to make sure Ginger didn't crash and burn completely. I left her curled up in the goat shed, depressed and alone. I, too, had to support the culture's growth in the right direction.

Book Two

Part 3

1

The Tipsytom morning air carried a reminiscence of the night and a foreshadowing of the day. The fragrance was shy and moody. The temperature vacillated between compassionately warm and nose-biting cold.

Daytime was a bazaar of active, noisy, shuffling scents driven like sheep, and above the chaos of the aromatic event was the syrupy weight of the pines, a burden on the eyelids in the midday heat.

The night had the smell of questions, of illusion, of evasiveness. As it always had, in all places, the night smelled of mystery.

Logan had become fearful of the mountain lions while I was away and I suggested that he had been in the wilderness too long.

2

A drop of water struck my forehead and I grumbled in my sleep. Half-conscious, I swung my arm up and apprehended the ticklish bead as it slid sideways towards my temple. I felt the childish despair that follows a disrupted sleep and nestled deeper into my sleeping bag. But there was no escape—the world was collapsing.

There was a gargantuan *CRASH* and I heard a thick grunt next to my ear, which I swear to this day was the sound of the earth beneath me enduring a fearsome blow. I shot up in alarm, tangled in my sleeping bag, and tumbled around in a panic until I extricated myself. One of the aluminum ridgepoles had folded and stabbed the earthen floor only a foot from where my head had been resting. It was embedded several inches into the ground. There was another explosive crash from the rear of the tent, behind the tarp wall where the weed was drying. It was another of the ridgepoles. I looked around in vapid terror, then perceived the water.

Everywhere—water was pouring into the tent and pooling on the floor. It gushed from the tarp that had once been the roof over the front third of the tent, but now hung heavily on the ground amid the bent and twisted aluminum poles. It poured in through low points under the walls, and it dripped through the grommets of the tarps. This all happened in a matter of seconds of course, and then I saw the tarp over the central section of the room. It was bulging down like a swollen balloon at the end of its strength and nearly brushing my hair.

"BROOKE!" I shouted frantically. "THE TENT IS COLLAPSING!"

I sprang to action, grabbing a wooden pole. I shoved the butt of it into the sagging mass of water trapped by the frame of the tent. I could hear it slosh over the side and collide with the ground. Water spewed beneath the wall where it landed. I darted to the other side and shoved at the second bag of water above the woodstove. Brooke, having come to life like a cannon ball, was faster to react than I, and with a heroic leap, thrust a kitchen knife through the laden bag hanging before me. The water exploded through the hole, ripping it wider, drenching us, and turning our floor to mud. Brooke lunged at the other sack of water and did the same. The frame, which had been leaning inward with threatening groans, seemed to sigh with relief as the water streamed into our home. Slipping and sliding barefoot through the mud and already soaked, we pressed water over the sides with poles, both of us putting our shoulders under the board and heaving with all our might. As the water poured off and the weight diminished, we were able to push greater quantities off, but the rain was coming down with such force that it immediately began to pool again.

Brooke was wide-eyed and breathing heavily, the kind of breathing that accompanies hyperventilation rather than exertion. "I don't want to poke any more holes in the roof. We gotta keep that water off."

I grabbed his arm. "Brooke, the back third collapsed too."

A look of horror gripped him. "The ganja!" he cried in pain.

We scrambled through the muck and into the interior chamber.

"NNNngg," Brooke choked, emitting a peculiar sound.

The plants were lying on the ground. One unfortunate stock had been mashed beneath the collapsed ridgepole. Brooke ran to it and pawed at it with heartbroken desperation.

"She's gone, Brooke, we gotta save the rest of them." I felt callous, but action was demanded.

Although the collapse of the backside was more complete than in the front, the land on that side sloped away from the tent and the water had run off the tarps and down the slope beyond. After a quick inspection, I could see that the plants were mostly dry, and only a little battered and dusty. I decided we could salvage most of them. Brooke pulled at his hair for a moment and then dove into a pile of tarps and rifled through them. He emerged with wild triumph holding a box of industrial-sized plastic garbage bags. He pulled the box away and threw it down, and even kicked it as an expression of his emotional overexertion. Then we began to bag the crop. Within five minutes, we had thirty thousand dollars worth of marijuana secured in bags and tucked under the table in the driest corner. Still, the rain bore down in heavy curtains of water, turning the land to soup. There was to be no peace that day, for there was still the garden to attend to.

I realized I was still in my underwear, so I pulled on a pair of pants before Brooke ran me into the rain and down to the garden. The plants had collapsed and most of the colas hung miserably from broken branches. Brooke was shaking his head as if trying to evict the image from his mind. He was clearly grieving. I had never seen him in such a state.

"We have to cut them all. If we don't we will lose the entire crop."

By the time Logan showed up, groggy and grumpy and looking for coffee, Brooke and I had turned the remaining third of the tent into a dry room with lines of wire running across it and the woodstove roaring like an enraged boar. We had eight plants hanging and were still barefoot and so wet that the water ran in steady streams from the crowns of our heads all the way down through the gullies between our toes.

"Goddammit, I left my shoes outside my tent last night and they are wet. I'm in a bad fuckin mood this morning."

It seemed as if Logan hadn't noticed anything was amiss. He yawned and ambled to the fire and began to stretch. "And it is wet as piss out there."

Brooke and I were off again, no time to converse. When we returned, each with a quarter of a plant across our shoulders, Logan was waiting in the new makeshift entrance we had propped up with a variety of wood pieces. He was wide-eyed and had a bottle of whiskey in his hand. "Looks like you boys need this!"

We passed the bottle around and each took a healthy slug.

"This might have to become a routine today," I muttered. My voice sounded coarse and I was shaking like a wet kitten. "It's not letting up out there."

And indeed, it was a routine. The whiskey kept us going through the day and night as we took it in shifts, pushing water from the roof, patching the holes that Brooke had inflicted on the tarps, re-stabilizing the structure with guylines and stakes, tying up the broken arms of the plants and then harvesting them when the tie-ups failed and the plants collapsed.

We were without infrastructure and now that something had gone wrong, it was painfully evident how unprepared we were. I thought of the various ingenious and inexpensive precautions taken by other farmers for situations just such as this: PVC hoops with tarps ready to be pulled over in moments, for instance. But in the Tipsytom Valley, we had nothing but a twenty-by-thirty-foot aluminum frame tent, now collapsed at both ends, and one car, hopelessly stuck in the mud. That was all.

Not only was there a failure of our human apparatus, the land itself seemed to come apart in the rain as if it, too, had been caught unprepared. We discovered that virtually all the high ground on the property was composed of clay, incapable of absorbing water. By evening, the trail to the garden was a sticky porridge of squelching goop—already shin deep.

By dark, there were sixty plants hanging in the now ten-by-twenty-foot space, and one woodstove we hoped would save the crop. We had begun to call our little corner of hell "Viet-tom."

All night we groped around with our headlamps on and broke

the plants down into smaller units, feeding the excess plant matter into the stove. The tent was a steamy sauna. We hoped to eliminate the density and moisture, and allow the plants as much space as possible. We hoped the plants would dry, and hoped that the feared mold would not infect them.

We covered the floor with scraps of tarp and spread weed across it. As more space opened up and the plants were broken into smaller sections, we ran more lines. We were obliged to crawl around the perimeter of the tent, avoiding the tarps, and staying beneath the hanging plants that occupied all the space above. But what else could we do? We were there because of the plants after all. They were everything.

After twenty hours of work, and feeling a cold mounting an attack on my system, I trudged through the mud to our car and woke Logan to take a shift at feeding the woodstove and pushing water from the roof.

3

Feeling like death was hovering around my shoulders, I dragged myself from the car after three hours of sleep and slopped back through a drizzling rain to the otherworldly tent. It felt like stepping into a movie scene where outlaw weed growers were hiding out in the hills and... *well,* I considered, *I guess that is essentially what's going on here. We look the part now.*

We certainly did look the part—disheveled, dirty, bits of plant matter in our hair and beards, bags under our eyes. If the farmers in the movies had working conditions like ours, I understood why they might be portrayed as deranged. There was nothing to see except marijuana on all sides, and water trickling through the poorly patched holes in the ceiling and into buckets. We had propped the ceiling with poles and it was necessary to take caution when moving around them because if one fell, likely the whole structure would collapse. Brooke emerged from under the table where he had been sleeping by the bagged plants, and Logan set to work starting a soup on the woodstove.

Famished, we stuffed most of our remaining provisions into a pot: onions, squash, kale, a few carrots, two boxes of macaroni and cheese, some oats, the dregs of a jar of peanut butter, a jar of black olives... and a half block of cheese that was actively aging... plus some home-canned salsa, and a jar of whole dill pickles.

While the mess cooked, we made a plan for the day—it would be another long one. We went out to charge the old car battery that Brooke had pulled from his broken-down rig, which was slowly becoming a plant nursery up at the top of the drive. We wanted to run the fans and a busted dehumidifier that Brooke was trying to fix. Logan and I connected the battery to our car and while we let the engine run, we inspected the driveway. Helga was stuck in the mud, but even if she hadn't been, the road was washed out in a section near the top. We were stranded. The Tipsytom felt like both a prison and a refuge.

Late in the afternoon, when we were sore from chopping wood for the fire, and we'd all gone down to leverage the remaining planting pots as close together as possible—so that we could build a makeshift cover for them—the clouds broke. In fact, they vanished and were replaced by a perfect rainbow that arced from one side of the valley to the other. Unbroken and rich. Brooke said nothing, but he opened his mouth as though he were going to drink it out of the sky. I breathed the kind of salubrious air that comes after a heavy rain and then scanned the beach. A vapor was rising from the earth and drifting towards the heavens and amidst this vapor was movement, a sort of popcorn popping activity. I puzzled for a moment and then followed the movement all the way to my mud-clad feet.

It was frogs, thousands of them. They had crawled from the waters all at once and were exploring their new world. The beach was so dense with frogs that it looked as if the land itself were coming to life. The world was turning into frogs. We trudged up to the tent in the last light, making our way through a low mist of youthful leaping amphibians. As we reached our destination, they began to sing.

That evening, Brooke hiked to the bar to call one of his land partners on the bar's telephone and tell him we needed help — disaster had come to the Tipsytom. When he came back, he said he had been in a forest of frogs the entire way.

4

We were huddled like urchins in the jungles of Viet-tom when Jona Charbeneau found us two days later and took firm control of the battlefield and the legions of battered and weary troops like a general, with energy, and goals, and a clear plan. Despite our worn state, we were obliged to step lively and comply with the program of the new campaign. That first day we grumbled under our breath with tired resentment as we shuttled supplies and tools down the washed-out drive. We were annoyed because we were relegated to the role of mere grunts after our heroic feats in battle. And we were annoyed that all our desperate technologies, with which we'd salvaged the farm, were second rate or became obsolete as Jona improved upon them or rejected them entirely. He deconstructed our works that had taken so much of our time and heart and energy. Our pride was hurt because we had survived the storm, and now our efforts seemed puerile and ineffective.

By evening however, when the tent was patched and secured, and several dehumidifiers were sucking up water, and several fans were cycling air through the plants, I accepted the reality that Viettom could not have gone on no matter how romantic it was, and that the improvements were desperately needed. As darkness fell and Jona treated us to burgers at the bar—with compassion and gratitude for our efforts—my umbrage dissolved.

As I digested the hamburger, which I consumed too rapidly, I studied the strange man that had come to our rescue. He looked awkward sitting across from me with a glass of beer in front of him. He looked awkward sitting in a chair. In fact, he looked awkward indoors. He was too expansive for the backwater tavern. Jona seemed confined by the walls and the ceiling and the conventions, no matter how rudimentary they were. It struck me that he was a man for whom time had become confused, and had spewed him into the world 150 years too late.

Although Jona Charbeneau may have been a cosmic mistake, he had come to terms with the world he lived in. Or rather, he had forced his terms upon the world. And if time was dragging him forward towards modernity, then he had dug his heels into the earth, and with equal strength, dragged time back to meet him.

Jona Charbeneau, Brooke Thatcher, and Nicolas Husk had purchased the forty-acre parcel in the Tipsytom Valley that spring and had gone into business together. The initial agreement was that Mr. Thatcher would see to the cultivation and management of the crops during the first season, and Mr. Charbeneau and Mr. Husk would provide financial backing.

It was Mr. Charbeneau who was our point of connection with the enterprise. He was from the same quiet and remote region of Oregon as Logan, Kay, and me, and it was through him that Logan

became involved. Mr. Charbeneau had been engaged in his own
activities in Humboldt County, but now that the situation in the
Tipsytom had fallen into a calamitous position, he had come to
confidently and competently resuscitate the farm.

I had met him only in passing at community events and knew
little more than he stood out visibly from other humans, and that he
had sired a child with a friend of mine. But I was to find that Mr.
Charbeneau was a singular and incomparably capable man. And he
solidified my belief that, in the great California wilderness, man still
holds the power of independence and self-sufficiency, and the
ability to govern himself.

Jona Charbeneau was tall and powerful and musky. And his
dreadlocks fell to his hips. His beard was a wild animal, but his
eyes were as soft and gentle as a baby deer's. He looked like a
frontiersmen and acted like one. He wore buckskins he'd made
from a buck he'd slain, skinned, tanned, and stitched. His collection
of knives was hilted with antler. He brought us gifts of wild
mushrooms and almonds in woven baskets of birch bark, and a
wild turkey he shot with a bow and arrow.

During all the time I spent with Jona Charbeneau, there was
never a task at which he balked or even cringed to undertake. At
each challenge, the first thing he assumed was that he could do it,
and after that, it was a simple step-by-step process until the chore
was completed.

His skills were extensive and he had learned them not from a
place of ego and a desire to impress others, but out of need and
practicality. His lifestyle demanded skills and tireless drive. He had
a calm faith in himself and, what was more, he had faith that others
around him could rise to the occasion and discover that they, too,
were surprisingly capable.

After the first full day when we'd done everything to secure the plants, the situation of the land was assessed, and we were squatting around a fire tearing turkey from the bone, Jona unveiled his plan in his stern, yet gentle and affable voice.

"I think we need shelter, boys. You guys need a secure place, and the plants need a secure place. Tomorrow we are going to start a cabin."

5

We built the cabin in eight days.

On the first day of the project, we selected the site, about thirty yards behind the tent where an old phone pole was whiling away the time with nothing to do. The location was screened by trees and therefore inconspicuous, but it also had a commanding view of the valley. So the abandoned pole became the corner post of the new cabin.

We climbed the mountain and cut sixteen stout and straight fir trees with a chainsaw, then shaved off their limbs with axes and saws. While Logan and I cleaned the poles, Jona took his truck to Lassy and returned in the evening with concrete, lumber, plywood, a few recycled windows, heavy gauge plastic, and stove pipe, along with an assortment of screws and nails and fasteners. Jona had every tool we could conceive of needing, and I was never clear on how they all fit into his truck. But I wasn't interested in questioning fortune.

I discovered that Jona's appreciation for primitive and traditional skills did not require excluding modern techniques. In fact, he adhered more to the philosophy of using everything you have and everything you need to get a job done quickly and effectively.

By the end of the second day, we had the poles in place and the bones of a 20-by-20-foot cabin. By the end of the third day, we were finishing the decking. By the fourth day, while filling the wall space with conventional framing, the sun came back.

We worked from dawn until dusk, and it was heavy, hands-on work, but it didn't feel like a job. We didn't leave at the end of the day and go home; we were working at home. And the only place we had to go was back to the jungles of Viet-tom where Brooke was despairing over the state of his butchered crop. We were designing and building a home for ourselves with what we had—trees from the land, a pile of recycled lumber, and a bit of new lumber. Besides the self-satisfaction of our ability to create shelter from what we could source, we needed it. At night, there were lightning storms in the mountains, and when we accompanied Jona up Rolltop Ridge to find a cell phone signal, the mountains seemed like shimmering teeth with the coming of the winter snow.

We needed the cabin in a human sense, and we needed it for our work to protect the crops that were our security and livelihood. It no longer felt like a job when everything in our lives depended on the completion of the task. The more we accomplished during the day, the more satisfied we were at night and the better we slept.

The situation on the land was fragile. More than ever, I felt as if we were in the wilderness. There were other people in the valley that might have given us shelter, but as far as the survival of the farm, the responsibility was ours and we were not prepared. The nearest supplies were far away in Lassy, and we couldn't even get our car up the hill.

Jona's coming had been a lesson to me regarding the values of the ganja-growing community—when your friends need help, put everything you could possibly need in your vehicle and go to them because there's nobody else to save them.

And in the wilderness, you must consider yourself their closest neighbor.

Jona seemed to accept this reality, maybe because he had been in our position before. It didn't matter that he had other business and another bigger and more lucrative farm far away waiting for his return. It was a value decision. He never discussed whether or not the year would be a success or a failure; he simply acted so that it no longer needed to be a question.

On the fifth day, when the rafters went up, Cassidy arrived. She was a girl I had started dating in Lassy, if you can term a relationship in the hills as dating. We spent infrequent moments of affection together. Her arrival cast a sudden spell across the land.

We had been living as if we were a penal colony. We were wild men without rules or sensitivity. We were defined by our brute qualities, and had abandoned social norms. Suddenly, a feminine sprite was drifting gracefully around the property, appearing in appropriate frames of golden leaves and gently curving boughs, or humming sweet and tender melodies down by the creek. We blushed and were embarrassed as we worked. We no longer farted and belched without consideration, and became aware of our personal odors. The feminine energy was a stark counter to the masculine desperation we had sunk into, and in the sunlight, we recalled that the world was fair. For the first time in many days, I remembered to take in the glorious beauty of the valley.

Cassidy made us sandwiches for lunch and we all felt like bashful schoolboys instead of weary homesteaders. We ate on the partially finished roof and watched a helicopter bob up and down over the ridgeline on the far side of the valley.

"What do you suppose that chopper is up to?" Logan pondered.

"Oh, those guys have been at work all season, although I

haven't seen them in the valley for at least a month," replied Brooke. "They are pulling out ganja from the National Forest. Who knows what they do with it once they pull it out... burn it somewhere I suppose."

"Smoke it," said Logan.

"Sell it," said Jona.

Brooke abruptly scampered down the ladder and trotted to the tent. When he came back, he had the remains of a newspaper. "Check out this column here."

We passed the paper around and scanned the contents. On one side was a perfunctory report of crimes committed in the county. Two articles, one on top of the other, told essentially the same story about the busts.

Marijuana plantation raided in National Forest... three thousand plants removed... Two Hispanic men spotted fleeing the crime scene; nobody apprehended... Degraded landscape... Garbage... Marijuana growing accessories confiscated....

The second article was almost identical except that it stated two thousand plants had been removed.

"Every week, from July onwards, the paper has two or three of these articles. Always the same," Brooke said, amused. "It's a good thing though—the government is doing it the right way. Those are all cartels from Latin America and they come in and put in as many plants as possible and divert streams, and use heavy fertilizers and pesticides. Bastards."

Brooke became suddenly agitated. "Nobody wants to smoke their chemical bullshit, and they are fucking up beautiful forests and dumping waste in the rivers. And they just leave a couple of poor farmers up there who aren't involved with the cartels at all and who are just trying to feed their families, so if one or two of their grows get busted, they don't care. Just a couple of hard-working guys they leave to fend for themselves. I think that is why the government doesn't try to arrest any of the people they see trying to get away." Brooke's voice had risen and he was flushed. His eyes were hyperactive.

"Bastards," Jona chuckled. "Well the one good thing about the cartel operations is that law enforcement has enough work busting them and they leave us alone. The little farms that are just growing their medical limit, small family farms like ours, aren't causing problems. So they just ignore us. They are more concerned about guns and international crime. It's also economics. The cartels are exporting the money they make out of the country, but we are boosting the economy here. Weed from all these small farms is bringing a shit ton of money into California, so they don't really want to bust us, unless you get too cocky and expand, or your neighbors get pissed off for some reason and report you."

Logan looked irked. "The neighbors pull that bullshit?"

Jona shrugged. "There are always people that have their feuds and don't mind wrecking someone else's life, but I have been doing this for a lot of years and it doesn't happen often. And now that the loopholes for growing legally are broadening, sometimes when the law comes, they just fine you for something else."

"Like what?" Logan asked.

Jona smiled. "Oh, like illegal structures and cabins and stuff."

On the sixth day, we sheathed the house with plywood and got the windows in, and the land was suddenly livelier. The trim crew arrived all at once, and though small, the population on the property suddenly doubled. Two of Brooke's friends from Oregon drove up in an old school bus converted into a home. They immediately got stuck in the mud and we spent a few hours trying to push it out and bellowing a great deal.

A couple of young girls from Wisconsin, daring wanderers who had fled troubled lives and discovered the liberal West and Brooke during a music festival that spring, arrived intent on making their presence noticed. The energy and the mixed personalities brought a level of chaos, excitement, and confusion.

On the seventh day, we weatherproofed the structure with tarpaper, and hung a plywood door while helicopters swarmed like bees over the ridge across the valley. On the eighth day, we moved the woodstove from the old crumpled tent into the new home, built a wood box with a trap door to the outside, and muscled and cursed the stovepipe into place. Then we declared the cabin complete and all of us traipsed to the bar to have more burgers and beers in celebration.

6

The following day, the wilderness of Viet-tom was abandoned and we began evolving a more refined form of living. We couldn't claim running water, and electricity was only available when we ran the generator Jona donated, but we felt like kings in our palace with the woodstove roaring and the weed hanging happily in the back half under a secure roof.

We spread out on the solid, even floor in the firelight while a stew simmered on the woodstove and Jona made chapatti bread. Cassidy gave us a lesson in Thai massage and used me for her demonstration. I winced and squirmed and cried plaintively as she wrenched my body into unfamiliar positions and calmly explained the methodology to her mesmerized audience.

Cassidy had been named for the ever-lovable outlaw, Butch Cassidy. She grew up blonde, blue-eyed, and pretty in Butch's old stomping grounds of southwest Colorado, and had spent a fair bit of time on horses. Like so many rural youth, Cassidy became bored and at the first open door to freedom, moved to Los Angeles to become a Candy-Raver and spend her nights high on Ecstasy and cocaine. She started stripping to fund her hobby and found that life a thrill until the rough side of reality placed her in dangerous and abusive situations. She had never lost her affection for horses or country music, so she left her darkening reality and found her way onto a dude ranch where she formed a relationship with a wise old woman who practiced yoga and loved Thailand. This woman influenced Cassidy to the extent that she abandoned drugs and horses, left her worldly possessions to charity, and moved to Southeast Asia where she devoted herself to yoga and massage.

Once Cassidy was educated in those arts, and clear in her intentions, she moved to California to rediscover drugs and horses by transporting large quantities of marijuana from California to a horse ranch in Texas run by some kind of local weed kingpin.

Kari looked at her wide-eyed. "You never got caught?"

Cassidy gently shook her head and shifted me, manipulating my tense and strained body. She placed a foot on my pelvis and pulled one of my ankles. There was a clicking noise deep in my groin and I gasped.

"Do you still do it?" Kari asked with crafty innocence.

Cassidy smiled. "No, I have joined the ranks of yoga instructors, masseuses, and energy healers setting up shop in Lassy... and I trim of course."

Kari studied the beautiful and enigmatic woman with awe, and maybe some jealousy. She began to stretch, and quietly watched the other occupants in the room.

Kari was a tiny creature. She and Shareen both claimed to be nineteen, but Kari looked about fifteen. Her hair was cropped almost to her head and had once been dyed red although the color had faded to orange. Her dark roots had recaptured most of her scalp. She had acne, but behind it was a perfectly symmetrical elfin face that I guessed would become striking as she matured. She was shy and flirtatious and insecure, and the most common sound I heard from her was a giggle that caused her mouth to smile before she could hide it away. Her eyes were watchful and I understood why after she mentioned she came from a poor family in Milwaukee with two drunken parents and three uneducated and conspiring brothers. She had run away from her troubled existence with Shareen, hoping there was something better in the West where the sun always went.

Shareen snorted, "And you're damn lucky you have a friend like me. Cuz you weren't coming out here alone."

Kari giggled and Shareen shrugged. "Just saying." She hopped up and sat down on Brooke's lap.

Shareen was a plump black girl with a story similar to Kari's, although she was a product of neglect rather than negative attention. Shareen had defiant eyes and was pleased to demonstrate that she had the romantic attention of the boss. She had committed to the hippy fashions of the prior generation and wore high leather boots and flowing dresses, but it was clearly an experiment like everything in her new life. She was willing to take risks and test waters to get what she wanted from a situation. She was young, and had found freedom, and as far as she could tell, there were no limits.

She bit Brooke's nose, "What's up with you? You're so damn quiet today."

Brooke had been sullen all week. He was worried about mold in the plants, but he also felt tense around Jona, who was decisive and dominant and intimidating to disagree with. Brooke may have felt dethroned and banished from his prior dominant role on the property. He had hardly worked on the cabin, preferring to spend most of his time loitering around the plants looking frazzled. I had asked him several days before if he needed any help with the plants and he responded absently, "Seems like the cabin is the thing to do these days." Now he sat staring at the woodstove with a blank expression and murmured incoherently only when Shareen tugged at his beard.

An off-key note from a guitar being plucked filled the momentary silence.

"Yeah, what's the deal, Brooke, you're as flat as this guitar you've been abusing."

The note warped and pitched and dived again before finding some equilibrium as Lena tuned it. Lena smiled at Shareen with dry pleasure, hoping for a shared chuckle. Shareen missed it.

"Well you'll be happy when we start trimming the bud. If not, I'm a slap a smile onto that face!" Shareen tapped his cheek playfully and Brooke stretched his lips into a meek smile.

"So what's up with you guys?" Shareen asked. "Drove that crazy yellow school bus down from Oregon?" Shareen was bored with the general calm and hoping to promote something interesting through conversation.

Lena concentrated on the guitar a moment longer and then replied in her plain, commonsense voice that was usually accompanied by a note of amusement. "Yep, us and that crazy yellow school bus." She plucked out a pattern on the guitar and began to sing. Her small-town voice turned into pure honey.

Lena had been a childhood friend of Brooke's and arrived with her partner, Tempo. They were hoping to make enough cash to spend the rest of the year traveling and performing. They were a music duet with a monthly gig at a college bar, but had hopes for a free-spirited road show with some fire dancing and homemade tunes, and maybe enough minor fame to pay the costs. Lena was content all the time, or at least she showed that side to the world. She was patient and practical, and easygoing. She was ready to say, *Sure, we can go trim pot*, and then move into a bus and leave her previous life of ease for a minor hope at something extraordinary.

Tempo listened carefully. "Lena, I think your F is flat, and you need to add that extra quarter-note at the end of the first stanza." Tempo's voice was uncharacteristically gentle and soft for his impressive size, but he spoke with the unintentional harshness of a scientist who sees only the facts of a situation.

Lena's eyebrows raised and her mouth scrunched into sardonic question. "Oh yeah? Well I'll just work on that, maestro!"

A sweet smile spread over Tempo's whole body and he lumbered over and scooped his girl into his arms. "I'm just trying to help you cuz I love you, honey, and I'm jealous because you sing like an angel and I don't!"

This was true. And he didn't play his viola like an angel either, despite his concentration.

Tempo was a black bear masquerading as a human. He was tall, but it was hard to tell at a distance because he was so thick that he just evened out and appeared average. His beard was immense and black as night, and cut off the lower half of his round face so that his countenance looked like a pale moon rising over a dark plateau. He wore tiny circular glasses and suspenders that made him look like an intellectual lumberjack, and possibly a cartoon come to life. His favorite morning greeting, which occurred when he and Lena woke and wandered down from the hill at about three in the afternoon, was to lift you up in a massive hug and walk you around for a time with your feet just off the ground as he inspected the condition of the property and brought you up to date on the latest scholarly information he had read in his astrophysics book the previous night. He was Venezuelan, a lousy musician, arrogant about his ability to chop firewood, and enjoyed knitting and making people smile.

Cassidy finished her demonstration and I was unable to move. Jona announced the commencement of dinner and the woodland creatures gathered at a distance to watch the softly glowing windows and listen to the cheerful ring of laughter from the calm security of the valley darkness.

7

Saucy Sally grabbed my hand and dragged me to the floor, pressing her folds of flesh against me and looping her arm around my waist. She twirled me around and cackled. "That's right," she called out, "my boyfriend's back!" This broadcast was inspired by the tune on the jukebox, "My Boyfriend's Back," by The Angels.

I caught Logan's eye and he gave me a thumbs up just as Sally tried to dip me. I fell over. She stooped to pick me up. She reeked of French fries and bad wine. Her sandy perm moved rigidly with her head, her sunken and twinkling eyes were mortared with makeup. She threatened to topple, so I jumped up and caught her and then swung her around several times for her delight. She emitted piercing shrieks of laughter and hugged me effusively when the song ended.

I retreated to the remains of my hamburger.

We weren't regulars at the Tipsytom Tavern, but we were definitely familiar faces, at least Logan and I were. Brooke didn't like the place because their version of vegetarian food was limited to grilled-cheese sandwiches, but Logan and I were devoted to their hamburgers. In fact, that was the only meal I ever ate there.

The scene at the tavern was as far removed from life on the

farm as we could hope for in such a remote hole in the earth as the Tipsytom Valley. In my mind, the place was perfect in every way because it bore no ambient similarity to our handmade home. The tavern was something to contrast the rest of my existence with, and it was undoubtedly the most social purlieu we had... actually, the only social one, unless you considered the frogs and jackrabbits.

It took us twenty minutes to walk down the river to the south and climb over the hump of land that stood between our home and the tavern. It was an enjoyable walk because we could arrive at the bar from the wild side and never see the road. On the livelier nights, the sounds of laughter and merriment grew and blossomed as we drew closer, and filled us with advanced excitement.

"YOU'RE A FUCKIN SLUT!"

There was a crash as glass exploded across the floor and added to its dark-stained patina—the lustrous coat that comes from years of expectorated chewing tobacco, spilled beer, and blood.

"Yeah, you heard me! Get outta here, YOU BASTARD!"

The miniature female swayed towards the door with her fists clenched, hollering imprecations at a loose-jawed hillbilly with a high forehead and gleeful bulging eyes.

"YOU'RE A FUCKIN SLUT!" she screamed again, finding the corner of the bar for support.

The hillbilly stood in the doorway laughing, and the more he laughed, the more his eyes bulged.

"Well, she got a tight cunt, and that's somethin you ain't!" He thrust his pelvis towards her several times.

His ribald response earned him a streak of spit on his pant leg.

The gnarled woman snorted and leaned back with exaggeration, preparing to project a second lugie. The man tried to run onto the porch, but stopped short as a small crowd of wary newcomers appeared with baggy street gear and San Francisco Giants hats. A splash of saliva hit the floor behind him and there was a moment of uncertainty.

"All right, which one of you is going?" Sandy, the bartender, stomped out from behind the bar and stuck her finger in the nose of the leather-faced, bloodshot-eyed little menace. "Wha'd I tell you when you came in here, Nancy? I told you to behave yourself, din I? It's a big night tonight!"

Indeed, it was a big night. The Tipsytom Tavern was hosting an open mic night, and already there were twice as many people as on a normal Friday evening. Logan and I had hustled out early to get our burgers and beers before the rush.

The cook, Jeff, a young man with a crew cut and a handful of hair on his upper lip was already twitchy when we arrived. He was running around the kitchen in an agitated state.

"Man, he is way too stressed about the crowds," I commented.

Logan focused on dressing his burger. "Nah, he's just high on meth."

Nancy had arrived earlier in a similar state, and joined the crowd of locals to smoke cigarettes with her toothless jaw bobbing up and down furiously until her ex had shown his offensive face and kindled a spirited row.

The smokers in the local community, which was all of them, always congregated in front of the *No Smoking* sign to have a cigarette. This was because Henry had his perch there and he was the patron saint of the bar. He was also the owner. Henry was imperturbable because he was always drunk and sleepy. He sat on a stool, chain-smoking Camel cigarettes with his back to the wall, the bathroom entrance on one side, the kitchen on the other, and the *No Smoking* sign above him. This position gave him an excellent view of the entrance at the far end, and of the glassy-eyed heads of elk, deer, and rams that lurked in the shadows of the rafters, about which Henry seemed to feel suspicion.

Logan and I paid our respects as usual, and Henry grinned with pleasure and told us of logging the valley in the old days. He rubbed a hand through his white goatee and flashed us his brown teeth.

"But now, there ain't much loggin. You either grow pot, cook meth, or make wine. It's just a valley of sin now."

We nodded solemnly while Jeff crashed and cursed his way around the kitchen, cooking something. We hoped it was our meal and not meth. We had heard Henry's discourse before, but we enjoyed it because the local community was so far removed in culture from the one we normally associated with and we felt it an important exchange.

"Yep, I cut my share of trees, and worked at the mill in Henly, three valleys over, for more than a decade before it shut down in ninety-seven. Hell, that was twelve years ago, I'll be damned." Henry paused to ponder this and light a new smoke. "But you know what, we're happy to have you boys around. We would have never thought it here, but marijuana has breathed a breath of fresh breath into the valley."

Logan and I both cocked our heads to make sure we'd gotten the message right.

"We like the newcomers, as long as they respect the locals… But we are all a big family here in the Tipsytom."

Logan lifted his glass. "Well here's to that! A big family and a breath of fresh breath."

I stifled a laugh by quaffing the last half of my beer. "Well, that's nice to hear you say, Henry," I said. "But there aren't many farmers in the valley. If this place fills up with growers and the locals become the minority, you think they will still feel comfortable?"

Henry flopped his head from side to side and lifted a hand in greeting to someone just entering. "I know, I know. There'll be more of you every year most likely, but it ain't bad for us to see a bit of the outside world. We can get a little... well, stuck sometimes. Tipsytom is a hard place to escape."

A group of mustached locals in lumberyard hats moved in to greet Henry and so we moved off to order another round of beers.

"Why the hell you mention that stuff?" Logan admonished me. "That's negative shit to plant in his head."

I felt guilty for a few minutes, and I sulked as we made our way to a table and sat down against the wall under a neon beer sign.

"Shit, Logo, that wasn't my intention, man, I'm just curious about all this stuff. I mean, it's kind of a crazy clash of cultures here and I want to know what they're feeling." I stopped Logan from interjecting. "I mean, what they are *really* feeling. Henry is a nice guy and he likes us because we come around and chat with him, but you think there aren't some people around who feel threatened? Some lady yelled at me last month in Lassy because her kid started smoking pot, so I know our profession isn't popular with everyone. Anyway, the Tipsytom Valley is gonna boom because of guys like that, not guys like us."

I nodded towards a short, stout, clean-cut man with a ruddy face. He was one of the big landholders in the valley. He owned the winery and the vineyards that graced the south face of the valley's slopes.

"Yeah, McKitrick might be their real enemy... Once he starts selling parcels of land," Logan admitted with a forgiving voice. "Just don't plant confrontational ideas in the local's heads because you have an obsession with cultural experiments."

I grinned and clinked my glass against his.

By the time the first curious growers floated silently into the large smoke-filled room, the place was already full of locals laughing and cursing and spitting on the floor, as was their custom. The rest of our farm finally arrived and the other nervous, isolated, and vastly outnumbered growers instinctively joined them in solidarity.

Nancy calmed down but grumbled audibly as she wandered off to play the Star Trek pinball machine in the corner and to chew on her gums. Henry was obliged to help Sandy behind the bar and leave his vigilant watch over the dull-eyed taxidermy. Jeff had scribbled the words *Vegetarian menu: Grilled Cheese with Pickle* on a piece of paper and taped it to the order window. Saucy Sally found another young man to flirt with. The rednecks played pool in the neon glow, and the pot farmers of sundry backgrounds formed alliances on the porch over shared joints and shared stories of the year's travails. The smell of cigarette smoke and ganja smoke mingled and locked fingers.

There was a clear distinction between the demographics—the two groups were from different realities, but already I could see the lines blurring and those realities merging, united by a common space. The locals were uncertain of the peculiar foreigners with strange garb and mannerisms and their aroma of cannabis, and the growers were unsure whether they were welcome, or resented by the locals. But on nights where the community opened its doors and invited the valley in for a gathering, the sides began to merge. An old logger or a local shop owner would saunter onto the porch and, after timid nods, join a cluster of rugged pot farmers to sample their favorite strain and to divulge that they, too, were growing a crop. And in the same way, a farmer might sit down by an old timer and offer to buy him a Coors, and then politely inquire of the denizen's knowledge of the valley's traditions. The interactions were cautious, but that was why the Tipsytom Tavern was such a fine venue for the introduction of two cultures—alcohol always greases social gears.

The open mic show was unorganized so in the end, Lena and Tempo played a show on the porch, and Jona accompanied them on a djembe drum that he sat in front of, cross-legged, in a trance, hammering out a rhythm. A didgeridoo showed up and filled the air with ululations. Inspired by the pained music, several hippy girls drifted into the space between the band and the onlookers, bending like willow trees with their hands above their heads and twirling in melancholy pirouettes. The local men immediately multiplied at the advent of this dance and stood leering with beers growing warm in their hands and cigarettes burning to the butt unnoticed.

A moment of near panic occurred when two girls suddenly sprang onto the stage swinging fire at the ends of chains. The locals drew back in alarm, and then broke into delighted laughter as the women spun and flailed the poi in hypnotic circles and loops, and it became clear that it was a performance and not arson. They pranced sensually across the deck, wreathing themselves in flames until it was too much for the local men.

"Yeeeeahhh! Light her ass on fire!" one of them cried ardently.

Hoots of laughter encouraged the remark.

"I'll show you how to make it hot, baby!" came another call from the ranks.

This inspired a slew of inappropriate comments and jokes from the hecklers. Cassidy and I looked at one another and cringed, but to my relief and pleasure, the fire-spinning girls laughed and one retorted that if the fire was making the men too hot, they would be happy to cool them down with a bucket of cold water. There were cheers of approval at this riposte and the scene reached a status of comfort. A drunken mandolin player from the valley joined the band and added a lively twang. Tempo abandoned his viola for a fire staff, spun it wildly above his head, and blew great bouts of flame into the air.

"He would make a nice rug in front of my hearth," someone observed, and the congregation on both sides laughed.

The mandolin player stamped his foot and Jona instinctively adapted to the rhythm. And then, with howls and clapping hands, the whole crowd began to dance and skip with the music.

Maybe the old logging families had never seen anything like the amusing invasion of circus druids who now occupied their homeland, but in the end, everyone was happy and smiling, and had no reason not to get along.

8

On the day Jona left, taking all of his marvelous tools with him, the dry room collapsed, Brooke was certain he saw the cougar, and the rain returned with unprecedented ferocity. Logan and I dug up a bag of rusty nails and retrieved our forlorn hand tools from under the cabin where we had stored all the hated items that reminded us of Viet-tom. We banged bent nails straight and then reinforced the drying racks and their support system. We also sighed a lot.

When the rain broke off the next day, we climbed into the cottonwood thicket to buck-up downed trees with a chainsaw, but Jona had taken the eye protection goggles so we used our snorkel masks. Once we had a sizeable stock of wood, we found that we didn't have enough tarp to cover it, so we scavenged scrap lumber and began building a shed off one wall of the cabin. But we didn't have a ladder anymore, so we chopped down a small tree and lashed cross pieces up its length. It took us a full day to build the ladder, and it was unreliable. But between that and the rain barrel, which contained our drinking water, we were able to erect a shed. Only once did Logan fall into the barrel.

The situation disintegrated from there. Logan stomped out of the cabin one rainy morning while I was applying tarpaper to an awning over the door.

"You seen the kitchen knife, Benji? I'm trying to prep some carrots and I can't find the fucking thing anywhere."

I looked sheepish. "Well, if you just let me finish cutting this tar paper, I'll clean it and get it back to you."

"Where is the god-damn screwdriver?" I called. Oil was leaking from the generator and the situation was clearly desperate.

A vague response reached my ears. "Give me a couple of minutes!" On cue, a couple of minutes later, Logan ran up breathless. "I had to get it from Tempo because he needed it to make a handle for the spatula head."

I nodded and Logan turned to leave.

"Wait a sec, why did the spatula need a new handle?"

Logan responded, pleased that he had the information I desired. "Well, Brooke broke the handle off because one of the switches for the fan stopped working in the dry room and that was the only thing we could fit into the mechanism to keep the fan running. It's all about the weed, ya know!"

I nodded again and Logan turned to leave once more as I looked at the oil spurting from the generator. "Wait a sec, what's Tempo cooking for lunch?"

Logan turned back confused. "He isn't cooking lunch. Why do you think that?"

"Because you said he needed the screwdriver as a handle for the spatula."

Logan seemed to see my logic and nodded gravely. "Honest mistake, honest mistake. You see, we needed the spatula head and a handle to use as a trowel." He hesitated, but my probing eyes had not left him so he felt compelled to continue. "You see, we poked holes in the bucket to make a shower, but then we realized we didn't have another bucket to carry water in, so we had to fill in the holes... and we borrowed that candle Cassidy gave you...."

I was glaring at him.

"I mean, we needed something to plug the holes," he appealed.

"Well what the hell are we gonna use as a spatula then?"

Logan rolled his eyes as though this were obvious. "I pulled one of the fins off your surfboard. There are no waves anywhere close to the Tipsytom...."

He was already running away.

Logan and I looked at one another with misery and humiliation. We looked like mutant raisins with pale arms and legs. We had purloined several of the black plastic garbage bags in which Brooke had stored the dried, but untrimmed, weed. Neither of us had clothing that was not saturated from our hours spent in the unremitting tempests of the Tipsytom, so we had endeavored to make rain repellent clothing.

I punched two holes for my legs in one bag, and cinched it around my waist, creating a diaper-like garment. In another bag, I punched holes for my arms and face so that it retained the properties of a hood. With a set of new threads for each of us, we set out to dig a drainage ditch so that all our possessions under the cabin would not have an aquatic existence.

"How is that spatula working as a shovel?" I asked sincerely.

Logan lifted it and tested it to make sure it was set well in the end of the healthy young branch. "Seems to do better as a shovel than a trowel. How is the screwdriver working?"

I was glum. "Terrible. I don't know why we thought we could use a screwdriver as a shovel. By the way, you look like an unhealthy turd."

Logan looked down at his pale legs distending obtrusively from his plastic diaper. He sighed. "Yeah, let's quit embarrassing ourselves. I'm sure the squirrels and foxes and ravens are all uncomfortable with this scene."

We spent the rest of the day naked, except for our boots, as we scraped out a ditch in the clay.

9

We managed to recycle the bags one last time to become fine Halloween costumes. Coupled with cardboard beaks and extra bags for wings, Logan and I became two handsome, bearded crows. Shareen took great pains with her outfit, and dressed as an Indian. She made Brooke strap a feather to his head and his eyes went into a darting frenzy with concern over potential inappropriateness.

"You know how people are in these parts. If they think you are culturally insensitive, they may shun you for your next three lives."

Shareen gripped Brooke's beard, which she used as a leash when she needed his submission. "Hold still while I put your face paint on."

Brooke winced as she applied black streaks beneath his eyes, and stared at us plaintively, begging us not to judge him. Lena wore a glittery wig, a sequin dress, and wings because she lived in a bus and had brought all her costumes with her. Kari looked jealous and morose and allowed Shareen to paint her face white and apply dark circles around her eyes to make them look hollow. After that, she looked dead and lonely. Tempo did nothing. He said he was going as a black bear.

Lassy was madness. Actually, Lassy was quiet as a ghost, but the party was madness. Everyone employed in the local marijuana industry was present. A synergy had formed over the previous months. No longer were the social gatherings awkward and unfamiliar, but rather the opposite. This event was a reunion and mid-season gala. Most folk were acquainted with the regulars of the community by then, but they had been busy at work, and now there was occasion to gather. In Lassy, it required little work to make a friend. If an introduction occurred, and time elapsed, the next time you occasioned on the person, you were long lost friends.

Anton and Jean greeted me with a bottle of absinthe and by the time we had caught up on the events of the season, I was drunk. Cassidy arrived, predictably dressed as a cowgirl, but she'd eaten a pot brownie and was incapable of communicating, so she went to sleep in a corner. Ginger made an absurdly false show of excitement when she saw me. She gave me a hug and beamed at me with affection, then introduced me to the poor lost chap who she boasted was her lover. She exhibited him to me like a trophy. Bobby, dressed as a robot, had a mistress, and remained in a corner most of the evening, whispering in her ear. Michael was having his usual edifying conversation with other serious growers. Ariel was laughing too loudly at Curvy Bend's insipid jokes. Curvy Bend had on his Richard Nixon mask once again. By every appearance, all the revelers had known one another for years and were overjoyed to be in the company of friends again.

By the time I flopped down on the pillows in the corner to soothe Cassidy, it was late and many had dropped the ghoulish masks from their faces and were wearing one another's lips and tongues instead. Farm life could be very lonely.

10

The weather had a dry stretch and we were able to repair the road to the degree that we liberated Helga. Lena and Tempo had been told of the volunteer fireman's fundraiser breakfast in the Tipsytom village at the community Commons that doubled as the fire department, so we drove Helga to the far end of the village to eat green eggs and ham, listen to Saucy Sally complain about some unrequited love, and hear Sparky pound away at an un-tuned piano.

We were the only outsiders at the event, and there was only so much we had to say about auto mechanics, so we drove to the little gas station store the locals considered the center of the village—a village clearly too small to have a center. We were hoping to find organic ice cream because Brooke was adamant about buying all things organic, no matter the price, and refused to fund them otherwise.

Logan and I were leaning against the car out front, watching the uneventful population center, when a truck pulled up and a Hispanic man hopped out. He looked intent upon running, but was unable to decide where to run. He spotted us and apparently found us non-threatening. He begged the use of our cell phone in broken English. We apologized and told him that as far as we knew, no cell phones functioned in the valley.

"You're off the map here, brother," said Logan, then, thinking for a moment, pulled out his wallet. "I've got a few bucks on this calling card though. You can use it at the payphone there."

The man hardly thanked him before bolting to the phone and with many frightened glances at the road started yelling into the receiver in rapid Spanish and running his hand through his hair in agitation. I looked at Logan. Logan looked at me.

"There was a helicopter over the ridge yesterday evening."

I nodded. "I know. Should we be helping him?"

Logan glanced back at the man. He was yelling again and so distressed that a blind man could have seen him shaking.

"I'm sure he is just a farmer like us, but I'm not sure if we are on the same side. You know?"

I nodded. The man abandoned the phone and returned Logan's card with a brisk nod, then jumped in the truck and roared off down the road towards the valley exit.

"Hmm, sometimes it's hard to know who's a bad guy and who's a good guy in this line of work, isn't it?"

11

The last plants had been harvested and trimming had taken over the cabin. Since Logan and I were not contributing to that enterprise, and because the mood was stressful, we found ourselves once again living out of doors.

The frost in the morning turned the grass to diamond spikes, and the trees had given up their annual fight and relinquished their bejeweled leaves to turn brown with the rest of the earth. The hidden glades and endless hollows of the land were suddenly exposed and their warm mysteries reduced to the cold sameness of winter.

Our only time in the cabin was the darkness before dawn. Logan would arrive first to make his coffee and start the woodstove, and when my intuition told me that there was an attractive cozy space waiting, I would run from my tent and kick off my shoes to appreciate the warmth and quiet of the pre-dawn hours and to eat a pre-breakfast bowl of oatmeal.

I recalled the yurt east of Garberville and the decadent sofas and carpets, and their woodstove that had given the palace a quaint rustic charm. With my limited experience, I had believed the Garberville property was the representative of all ganja farms, but now I was becoming versed in the variations of the society within which I was living, and I was learning that the marijuana farming community was far more complex. This new society was diverse, varied, and pieced together by individuals of every idea, orientation, and background. It was our common activities and our near proximity that allowed us to adopt common traits and evolve into something unique that stood out from the rest of society. If I had been forced to choose at that point, I would not have left my woodstove in the Tipsytom valley for the grandness of the yurt. I was at home.

Logan craved his mornings so deeply that his sleep schedule became frightening and bizarre. He began to wake earlier and earlier, and truck towards bed at preposterous hours. When his habits reached their worst, he would pop his head into the cabin at five in the evening as we prepared dinner, already in his fleece sweatpants and announce that he was off to bed. He admitted one morning when I arrived at four-thirty that he had been up since two o'clock.

When the first light slid over the battlements of the hills, we would embark on our daily routine and march up the mountain to fill buckets of water from a filter box we had constructed around a natural spring. We would break our first sweat bearing the buckets back to the cabin to replenish the drinking water and wash the dishes in the ice-crusted water of the outdoor sink set up against the cabin wall. When the chores were done, I would climb the hill to watch the sun rise, a little further to the south every day, and feel the winter moodiness that inhabited the wilderness and wonder— for a second year—what to do when the season ended.

Once the sun found the valley floor, Logan and I would reconvene on the beach and dive into the freezing waters of the creek. Our howls and screams were the alarm clock for the rest of the camp. By the time they appeared in the cabin, we had breakfast waiting and were enjoying our second sit before the fire.

12

Brooke continued to spend hours obsessing about mold and sorting through the weed with a headlamp. Sometimes the stress got to him so much that his eyes would dart around and he would pace and declare that the crop was ruined. Lena would calmly roll a joint of Trainwreck, which was the only strain that seemed to calm him down, and make him smoke it. Then his eyes would steady and he would become cheerful and start singing one of the little jingles he had invented concerning his trade. *"Trim a bale, trim a bale, trim a bale of ganja, trim it till the sun goes down!"* or some other repetitive and annoying rhyme that went on and on.

On occasion, I could get him out for a walk in the woods and he would regain his composure.

"Brooke, you're getting cabin fever. You've been here too long. Maybe you should take a day for yourself. Take a silent day! I did one, I was inspired by Rubicon—it helps a lot! Or take Shareen to Lassy for a day. I dunno, but don't let the weed drive you crazy!"

Brooke scowled. "Shareen and I broke up. I think she and Kari are gonna take off soon." He was silent as we crunched through the leaves. "But the mold is gonna spread, the LA Kush is full of it. It's frightening to put all of your resources into something. If the farm fails this year, I'm ruined."

That was the terrifying reality for many ganja farmers during their first year. I recognized that I couldn't understand the stress because I hadn't given everything to it; I wasn't putting everything on the line. Getting your plants to their mature state was one task that could have conditional or legal problems, then harvesting and getting them trimmed was another task with different conditional or legal problems, and then there was getting rid of the finished product, which was the riskiest of all. I knew Brooke had not yet figured that part out. I wanted to say something to console him, but I didn't have any valid lectures on that topic, so I patted him on the shoulder.

But his obsessions drove us out, and Logan and I spent many dark, wet afternoons just sitting in our car or huddled in the woodshed drinking malt liquor and talking about women. Just as Brooke needed a holiday and an escape, so did we. The farm was our entire life.

When the weed was finally sorted, and Tempo and Lena were within sight of the end, Brooke switched to sorting almonds.

13

The fog hung on the river plane like an old woman's shawl. We traipsed across the loose river stone and through the thickets trying to embody the silence around us. Logan was successful, but I was a blundering mess. If I walked, I didn't see; if I listened, I didn't move; if I looked, I couldn't hear. Our stealth was, as I feared, feeble. By the time we found an adequate view of the wetland, all we saw of our quarry were their tail feathers disappearing down the watercourse.

"So much for duck soup," said Logan in a hoarse voice. He took a potshot at a jackrabbit with the pellet gun, but that was equally unsuccessful. "We are terrible hunters. Let's go down to the river."

We crossed the broad gravel flats and pushed through the brush. It was late in the year for salmon, but lying on the rocks, almost at our feet, dying in the shallows, was the largest salmon I had ever seen. Its open mouth revealed ancient crooked teeth; its cold eye was watching us. Logan grabbed my arm and stifled a gasp, then muttered silently. "That thing has to be fifty pounds."

We sat and watched the fish struggle for a time and finally make its way back into the current of the Triumph River, pointing its ancient hooked nose up river.

"Goodbye, wilderness." Logan saluted the leviathan.

We trudged home to cook a greasy breakfast.

Every drop of rain splashed a bit of the blues onto my boots as I walked away from the little home I had built. I looked down at the remote cabin with the thread of smoke trailing from the chimney. It looked so alone and yet completely natural in the Tipsytom wilds. I couldn't recall what the valley looked like without it.

Rolltop Ridge wouldn't let us out—the snow had slunk in and closed the way. We'd have to take the icy gravel road to Lassy.

We passed Henry sitting in front of the bar and I rolled down the driver-side window.

"Hope to see you next season, Henry. Don't let the bar wash away while we're gone."

He smiled brightly, "Well, you'll be welcome back. We will be right where you left us. And holy shit! You hear that Sparky caught a forty-seven pound salmon at the bridge?"

Book Three: Runaway Transitions (Fall & Winter 2010/Spring2011)

Part 1

1

There was a yurt. The farm had earned its first yurt. I wondered if there was a secret committee somewhere that issued one yurt to each farm that survived to maturity.

Perhaps they gathered annually in Tahiti at the end of the season and read through the reports on every upstart landholder who thought he could make a living as a farmer. Some received a golden stamp on their portfolio and were granted permission to erect a Mongolian nomad's shelter. It was a badge of accomplishment. Once a yurt was present, it was a bona fide pot farm.

There was a dead deer hanging under a shade structure and I walked over to inspect. It looked down at me with soft, innocent eyes that said, "Isn't life wonderful?" It was a beautiful young thing, probably a yearling. It looked fit and fine, then it slowly twisted and exposed the side that had been struck by a vehicle.

"Charbeneau found it up on Rolltop this morning. He is going to teach Hanna to skin it later today. Then we'ree gonna have a paaaarrrtyyy!"

I had never heard Jona called by his last name and it sounded awkward. Men like Jona had last names only as a formality, for paperwork and such.

A lanky young man wearing tight jeans and a baggy jean jacket stood behind me. He was in open air, under the broad light of a midday sun, but managed to appear as if he were lurking. His hands were stuffed in his pockets and he was hunched over like he was trying to keep warm while smoking a cigarette outside a concert venue on a cold night. He lifted an eyebrow.

"I'm Aaron. I don't fit in here with these spiritual mountain folk, I know, I know... eerrr, you must be Benji." Apparently, he was worried his off-kilter humor had fallen on sensitive ears.

I smiled and shook his hand. "Charbeneau is over where you hear the commotion."

There was indeed the sound of activity beyond the bushes. Aaron stared at me for a minute expectantly, for what I had no idea. "Ok, see ya," he said and shuffled off towards the garden.

Suddenly I felt foreign on the familiar little farm. The place I had helped build from the ground up the previous year was almost unrecognizable. I walked past the glossy, boastful yurt and found the cabin. It had been dressed up with various tarp additions and looked like a refugee camp. The space around the cabin appeared to be more actively used than the interior. There was an outdoor kitchen under one tarp roof; drying screens with pears and plums under another. A pretty girl was standing at an easel painting under a third. She glanced at me with disinterest, then resumed her art. I stood in the sun, squinting, and scanned the scene.

New structures had been erected in areas that had been

wilderness the previous year and there were sounds of activity in every direction. There were more people than I had ever seen on the land at one time, and not a single familiar face. I had wandered the desolate wilds of Northern California once again in search of the small scratch on the map that was the Tipsytom Valley and, upon discovering it, found that it was home to a bustling civilization of eager and energetic youth. I was overwhelmed and not sure if I liked the changes.

Several pretty girls were doing Yoga on the hard-packed earth near the cabin, and another pretty girl walked by with a basket of fresh, leafy vegetables. I turned and walked towards the creek. A terrace had been crudely formed on the hillside above the beach—apparently the new weed garden. The plants were twice the size of what had been grown the previous year, and they looked full and healthy and well tended. Aaron and a pretty girl were pruning them as I passed. I smiled and walked through the bushes to the beach. A tanning rack and a pile of deer hides were on one side of me, and a naked man with a guitar playing a song to two pretty, naked girls on a blanket on the other side. One pretty girl was standing in front of me in the creek, naked. She looked over her shoulder at me and smiled. Her butt cheeks blushed, and she dove into the water. *Ok, I like the changes around here,* I thought.

Jona and his four-year-old son, Ezra, emerged from another access to the beach, some ways away. Laughing and distracted, they stripped off their clothes and dove into the creek. I dropped my garments and plunged in.

"Benji!" Jona shouted with delighted laughter. "Welcome! What do you think? How do things look around here?"

"Different! Good! It feels alive."

He nodded with a smile and his voice rumbled gently across the water. "We have been manifesting good things, lots of activity, lots of new people! We have a community on the land now! It's feeling super positive, yeah, lots of full power people and strong energy!" He nodded in agreement with himself. Jona was excited and proud.

"Benji, this is Isabelle," Jona said. "She is out here from Florida." The pretty girl with the blushing butt cheeks doggy-paddled over, beaming.

"Hi, nice to meet you."

I blushed a bit myself. Yeah, I liked the changes.

We added ourselves to the collection of naked people on the blanket and sprawled in the sun while the man with the guitar wheedled.

"The valley is a different place than it was last year during the days of Viet-tom, Benji. It kind of seems like it has been discovered by the outside, well, at least by the brave ones." Jona was running his hands through the hair of a demure, yet striking blonde, and he smiled at her and winked. "Last January, the California Supreme Court lifted a couple of bylaws that were putting pressure on the farmers, and everyone is a bit more relaxed right now. Not sure if it is good or bad, but people are flooding into the region and buying up any land they can find. It sounds like at the end of the month Governor Schwarzenegger is going to sign something else that reduces punishment for possession. I think it makes possession an infraction instead of a misdemeanor, which is like, practically legal. So the loopholes just keep getting bigger and people feel safer. It's bringing lots of amazing people from all over."

I looked around at the naked bodies sprawled in over-dramatic leisure.

"A big international influx now," Jona informed. "There has been something of an international community down in Humboldt for a long time, but it seems to be growing and spreading. We have

Germany and Austria here right now." He laughed happily and nodded at one of the other women dozing on the blanket. "And we have Florida, of course!"

Isabelle giggled.

"But it might all fall apart in November," said the man with the guitar who turned out to be a friend of Jona's, visiting from Grass Valley, and also a marijuana farmer. "They will vote on Proposition 19 to make it legal, and then it's all going to change."

The man looked agitated and I wondered how that was possible given the current situation and the attractive company.

"It could change things for the better," Jona posed.

"No way! The loopholes are perfect for us small, organic farmers. As soon as it goes legal, the corporations will get all the permits and monopolize the industry. Philip Morris and all of those other fucking cigarette companies are waiting with their fingers on the buttons to start the mass production. I've heard they have big warehouses in southern California all set up. As soon as the law passes, the lights go on." The man sneered. "It's what all law enforcement is pushing for. It's what the state wants. They want to tax the hell out of it to deal with the fucked economy. It's actually the growers who don't want it."

The pretty girl who had been carrying the vegetables arrived and took her clothing off. "That's not true!" Her accent was distinctly Germanic. She began stretching. "A lot of farmers I know want it to be legal because it should be legal. It's not hurting anyone."

Jona nodded. "It should be legal. I don't think the small farms would go away. Weed is a connoisseur's substance. Some people would buy cheap name-brand stuff, but quality matters with ganja. There will always be demand for high quality organic. Just might drive prices down a bit."

The visitor scoffed. "Ha! I'm sorry, my friend, that is very optimistic, but there is too much money in this industry. It's gonna go the way of everything else—owned by fucking corporations. It's just a matter of how and when. If it's not in November, it's gonna be in the next few years."

I lost interest as another svelte young woman walked to the shore, casually removed her clothing, and slid into the water. *How could they be talking about laws and politics?*

"Well, we all know it is a dream to be in this place at this time, and that it probably won't go forever, so let's enjoy it now! Benji, we are building a new outdoor kitchen—pole-frame structure. You have some energy to help me get a few rafters up?"

I sighed and looked at the setting, then collected my clothes and followed Jona away from the beach of fantasies to do manual labor. *I sure hope this life sticks around for a while. Who cares what the laws say?*

Nature provides, and the vast freedom of the Tipsytom wilderness was abundant with blossoming females. It certainly made me feel like I should embrace the wild in me. To acknowledge this savage element of life, I set up camp in the old mountain lion den, now long abandoned. It turned out to be a mistake because a family of spotted skunks moved in under my sleeping deck by the end of the month and the wood rats in the region ate my leather shoes.

2

We skinned the deer. I cut off its head with a hatchet, cracked open the skull and scooped out the brains. I mixed them with egg yolks, then mashed them into a paste. I decided to leave the fur on one side, and so I globbed the brain paste onto the bare side of the young deer's skin and worked it in with my hands. Once the hide was well coated, I spent three hours pulling it vigorously across the sharp edge of a board and batting away the maddened flies that urgently wanted to lay eggs in any dark, damp, meaty crevice. Finally, I stretched the hide on a small rack to dry. In the end, I had a baby deer rug, well, more of a deer door mat, and I wasn't sure that was something I should boast about.

During the time I'd spent with the hide, Jona and Hanna had processed the meat and Hanna had managed to score one of Jona's knuckles to the bone with a knife. The young deer was going to provide for an excellent *paaaarrrttyy* and, I hoped, keep my feet warm on cold winter nights.

Hanna stared at me with a hollow smile and showed me her bloody hands. The image seemed more fitting the longer I knew her. "We have lots and lots of meat!" she said in a thick Bavarian accent, then watched my reaction. "And where is Isabelle?" she added with a smirk.

The deer was the first of three road kill that we processed that season. The baby deer made for an ample full moon feast. The big buck we brought in two weeks later fed the farm for most of the month. Ezra made off with the severed head and played with it for a week until Jona confiscated it. And the mother deer, completing the family, we dragged off the road when we were leaving the land for the end-of-season celebration on the coast. We processed it as a circle of chanting hippies high on LSD before it disappeared into somebody's freezer.

People began to arrive for the full moon feast, and the quiet little farm in the hidden valley buzzed with energy. I had been there almost a week and still wasn't sure who was living on the farm and who was just visiting. There seemed to be a constant flow of people coming and going every day. Men seemed to come, and pretty girls seemed to go. I let them come and go—it was part of the reality in that country. People came and went very quickly.

I had found a distraction in Isabelle and I wasn't terribly troubled about who else was permanent or impermanent. The crewmembers would become clear as the season progressed.

It was the first time I had attended a party on the land, but I wasn't particularly concerned with it. I had spent the last few days constructing dry rooms in preparation for the weather we knew would eventually come, covering hoop houses in massive tarps, sealing seams with a heat gun, setting up new structures for extra drying space, and running power lines across the property. The quantity of marijuana far exceeded that of the previous year and we needed dry space to hang the harvest, structures that would not collapse in the rain.

The paramount technological advancement on the farm that had elevated its status in my eyes far more than a yurt ever could, was hot water. I continued to bathe in the creek until late November when the frost was sprinkling diamonds on the grass, but this tradition was enhanced by the knowledge that a hot bath was available. I discovered I deeply loved a piping hot bath beneath a starry sky.

An old clawfoot tub had been placed in the earth near the shower and partitioned from the rest of the terrestrial world with bamboo mats. As the stars emerged and friends and neighbors from the surrounding vales and hillsides converged on our farm, my attention was focused on the tub. In my mind, this was a triumph and the indicator that the farm was a success. There was now leisure and relaxation.

Isabelle peeked around the corner. "Is the bath full? I'll be right there. I have a treat!" she giggled and scampered into the darkness.

I sat in the water, wincing with pleasure in the heat. I tilted my head back against the cold rim of the tub and looked up at the stars, then closed my eyes. I felt soft lips press themselves against mine.

"Scoot forward and let me in," Isabelle whispered.

I complied, and a soft body settled into the bath behind me.

"Open your mouth," she said.

I complied with this as well. Something dense and wet settled on my tongue. I bit down experimentally—blood!

Isabelle burst into a fit of giggles. "I brought you the deer heart!"

I chewed the raw organ thoughtfully while the hot water exhaled and filled the air with its steamy breath, and gentle arms wrapped themselves around my chest.

"I brought seared strips of backstrap too," she said sweetly. "Not just a raw heart. Jona said it's the best cut."

I lay in the hot water beneath the stars in the arms of a beautiful woman and let her feed me lightly seared baby venison. Certainly, it was no longer the days of Viet-tom.

3

The young deer transitioned to a thing of memory. Several vegetarians who felt comfortable eating wild game were dealing with painful gastrointestinal problems. The kids had been put to bed. And most others had drifted off to their own quiet corners of the land. Bobby had arrived late in the party, reminding me that the community was still small and somewhat familiar. It turned out that he was dating Isabelle's sister, Tiffany, the painter. I didn't talk with him very long before Tiffany dragged him away. Those who remained, sat around the fire.

Fires are a mesmerizing trap. In capacious spaces such as the Northern California wilderness where the dark of night is complete, the party invariably turns to the fire and the mood frequently turns to solemn contemplation accompanied by the soft pop of burning wood. I missed Brooke. He would have produced a guitar and belted out some haphazard Bob Dylan songs, but he was living a couple of valleys over at his girlfriend's farm that season. None of the familiar characters of the previous year was there. I looked at the illuminated faces: my new community. It was a group that had no common history, didn't know one another, and yet would learn to cooperate, work together, and live together as a family. It was a strange experiment.

"I sink I vill be Jona's lover," Hanna abruptly announced. "I feel it in my heart chakra." Hanna looked smug.

Mara looked up and there was an extra fire in her eyes, beyond the reflection of the one she was crouched in front of. Aaron smirked with amusement.

Isabelle giggled. "I think you feel it in your sacral chakra!" Her joke caused her giggles to increase, and she snorted several times.

Hanna pretended she hadn't heard. "He doesn't know it yet, but he vill fall in love with me!" She stared into the flames with a benign smile and shifted her hips side to side like a teenage girl fantasizing about the latest school heartthrob.

"Ooh, Jona! All the girls love Jona!" Isabelle cooed.

Mara continued to watch Hanna, the fire in her eyes chilling as ice.

Hanna looked at Isabelle. "What? You love him too? I sink you don't have the opportunity."

The vibe at the fire veered in a strange direction. I slipped my hand around Isabelle, feeling protective and insecure.

Hanna abruptly stood and spun around, her genie pants flared, and she laughed without humor. "It is not a competition! It is simply a fact zat he vill fall in love with me! I see it in the stars!"

Mara snorted and walked into the darkness.

Suddenly, a sunny face ringed by rich ginger hair emerged in the light. "Hey, guys! How's it going? Don't we have some guitars or something?"

Thank god! I thought. I liked this guy.

Hunter had shown up that day. He was a jovial boy from Iowa who had no connection to the farm and had simply walked down the driveway from parts unknown and asked for work. Jona, with an eye for a good worker, had simply put a shovel in his hand and asked him to dig a ditch, which Hunter had joyously done… all day.

Isabelle shrieked by my ear. "Yeeeaah! Music! There are two really shitty guitars in the yurt!"

I winked at Hunter. "Know any Bob Dylan? I can probably play along."

4

A new and extensive vegetable garden had been planted just beyond the cedar grove. That was Mara's world. She was German, and her efficiency was appropriate to her heritage. She ruled her kale, strawberries, and squash with a kindly yet strict, unquestionable authority. I always asked permission to enter the garden before going in. She would laugh semi-convincingly and tell me that I didn't need permission, as it was the community's garden. But the first time I had walked into it without asking permission, I saw her eyes narrow and a cloud pass across the sun.

Mara was a renaissance woman. She made her own clothing,

and made the handles of her gardening accouterments from fallen branches. On occasion, she would disappear for a day and return with fresh fish. She made strange medicinal elixirs and tonics from wild plants; canned fruits and vegetables; and made delicious, sugar-free desserts. She was also an aficionado of the didgeridoo and was pretty enough to make the instrument look surprisingly sexy.

"Ya, you can put it on your skin too, you know? It's very good for you."

Isabelle regarded the tall German woman with adoration, and lapped up everything Mara had to offer. They were in the new and functional outdoor kitchen we had just completed. Mara was teaching Isabelle to put turmeric on her face (a beauty care product in those lands) and they both looked like grinning Halloween pumpkins. Isabelle was our cook, and the kitchen was her domain—in theory. But in reality, the kitchen was part of Mara's domain and Isabelle just worked there. Isabelle would spend the day massaging kale and stringing chili peppers to dry, and then Mara would arrive at dusk and suddenly delightful aromas would drift to any corner of the farm we happened to inhabit at the moment, no matter how far, beckoning us to eat. We would already be walking towards the kitchen when Isabelle clanked the rude metal triangle that was our dinner bell.

Upon sitting down, Mara would announce how brilliant Isabelle was in the kitchen, and Isabelle would blush beneath her orange turmeric mask, which had become her daily costume. Mara took credit only for the dessert.

"Izzy, you are getting so creative with quinoa and lentils! And the salad dressing is perfect."

Isabelle looked shy. "Thaanks, Tiff, but really it's Mara."

Tiffany reached over and tried to wipe turmeric from her sister's face. She seemed to think that her little sister needed management and rearing and regular boosts of confidence.

Tiffany managed the cannabis garden when Nick Husk wasn't around, which was most of the time. She was a striking girl, perpetually tan from a life under the Florida sun, and had been a cheerleader in high school until she discovered pot. After that, she was an artist. She was moody and secretive, and didn't like it when I said good morning to her. She was usually visible only when she was working with the plants or eating dinner. Otherwise, she was ensconced in some gloomy hollow painting still-life pictures.

Tiffany was my peculiar link to the previous year. Not only was she dating Bobby, but she had also worked for Ginger, who, Tiffany told me, was pregnant, and now, justifiably large. Oddly, it was through this that we bonded.

Tiffany understood that part of her payment from Ginger was a queen-sized mattress of passable quality, as she had seen no currency of another kind. Tiffany had taken it when she left Balsam Hill. Ginger, enraged that anyone would expect anything of her beyond the gift of being in her presence and witnessing her vast beauty, sent one of her minions, indeed her only minion at that point—the one now eternally chained to her by a common fetus—to extinguish the rebellious girl's spirit, and retrieve the now mildew-speckled bed.

"Where is Tiffany?"

I turned to find a man I had never seen before standing in the kitchen. I was making myself a peanut butter, jelly, and egg sandwich and the aggression in the man's voice caused me to break the yolk. I looked at him for a moment. His chest was puffed out, and his jaw set with righteousness. It pissed me off.

"Well, what do you need her for?"

"That's none of your business. I need to see her now."

I nodded and smiled. "Well, you see, it is my business, because if you come to my home and make demands before you even introduce yourself, I'm going to see you as a threat, and I am going to be protective of my people. So you can start over, tell me who you are, tell me why you need to see Tiffany, and then we will see."

He fidgeted and looked uncomfortable and clearly startled by my opposition. He had just broken a number of unwritten laws of respect in the ganja world: it is very bad form for a stranger to show up unannounced in a place where the activities are of questionable legality, and aggression as a form of communication is something Neanderthals did, not enlightened Earth people.

"Uh, I'm Mark. Tiffany is in debt to my partner, Ginger, and I have come to collect that debt."

Ginger! Suddenly I could plainly hear her voice behind his words. He was just a peon, a physical manifestation of Ginger's anger. A carrier pigeon.

"Ok, I'll go with you," I said.

He began to protest, but I ignored him and walked towards Tiffany's encampment. As his words were not his own, and he was a puppet with a mouth, he had no control over his conduct, and I had no intention of allowing him to corner Tiff.

"I have come for the bed. You stole it from Ginger. You are lucky that all she wants is the bed and not money. You are completely irresponsible. You are a liar and a thief!"

Tiffany, caught unawares, gaped, then tried to defend herself. "What? I worked for her every day for a month and she told me my payment was all of the food I had eaten and the bed that I had slept on. I even asked her if I could take it, and she said she wasn't going to sleep on a mattress that someone else was using. So I took it! She wants money from me? I mean, that's...."

"Don't try to manipulate me!" Mark said, and I could hear Ginger's voice again. He was repeating what he had been instructed to say, or possibly worse—channeling! "You were taking advantage of her because she needed help at the time and then when you saw she was in her power, you ran away like a coward... and you stole her mattress. It was a $300 bed."

Tiffany looked wounded and shocked, and baffled by the assault. I was starting to feel dangerous, so I intervened with words before my communication turned physical.

"Mark, I told you once already that you don't come on our property and make demands. Now you are attacking my friend and my community. It sounds to me like the deal is closed. And since you aren't treating people with respect, I am going to escort you off the property."

They both looked at me with shock. I was smoldering.

"I, I could just give back the stupid mattress," Tiffany started.

"No, you can't," I said.

Mark seemed to come to his senses. Ginger's hypnosis had taken a blow and her messenger vaguely grasped that he was yet again breaking the code of conduct. He looked confused.

"You can pass a message on to Ginger. Tell her that the mattress can cover the rest of what she owes Tiffany. If that is ok with you, Tiff, and if you're willing to settle for only a mattress."

She still looked shocked. "I just don't want to deal with that crazy lady anymore," she said.

I walked Mark up the hill and he didn't protest. He seemed to be going through an internal struggle. Near the top of the hill, before we reached his car, he finally spoke.

"Look, sorry, man, I was just the messenger here."

"I know," I nodded.

Ginger was in the passenger seat of the car, wedged in, filling the crannies and crevices. She saw me and glowered. As I drew near, she carefully composed a sweet façade.

"Hello, Ginger."

"Oh, Ben! I didn't know you had been able to find work in this area. I'm so happy someone has taken you in. This is my lover, Mark." She introduced him as though he was a belonging and it was her prerogative to make his introductions for him.

"We met," I said.

She looked at him. "Honey, where is the mattress?" Her voice was of the calm that heralds a storm.

"There is no mattress, Ginger, Mark can explain. I have work to do so I'll let you show yourself off the land. All the best."

She looked at Mark with a curious kind of loathing.

I left.

Tiffany seemed comfortable with me after that, and told me on several occasions that she appreciated me looking after her sister, which was not at all the reality of the situation.

"C'mon, Aaron, we have to finish tying up those Mr. Nice tonight. The stems are gonna break if we don't." Tiffany tried to express the gravity of this by looking wide-eyed at Aaron and shaking her head as though to say, *Do you want all of the Mr. Nice plants to slump in the dirt?*

Aaron rolled his eyes so forcefully that they could have knocked over bowling pins. "Only if you are Mr. Nice to me when you ask!" he quipped with sassy softness. He rocked back in his chair and then launched himself from the shadows where he had been peering at us with Gollum eyes, an unsuccessful menace. He rose as a gangly mess, the tightness of his pants seeming to be the only thing that stabilized him. "You're all weird!" he stated and followed Tiffany from the kitchen.

Aaron was also from Florida, and from the same general friend community as Izzy and Tiff. He had the peculiar title of *gardening intern*, a role Nick fabricated and I never understood. He hovered around Tiffany during the day, skulked in the shadows in the evening, and occasionally unpacked an electric guitar with an effects board and produced pained noises. Sometimes he would fill interludes with adjectives and then chuckle and state that he had "waxed poetic." He was never interested in clear conversation, and if you tried to chat, he would stare at you intently then slowly lean closer until you could smell his breath and had to withdraw. Or, on occasion, he would gently run his fingers through your hair in a disconcerting manner. He held some kind of disdain for Jona because, well, Jona was good at everything and recognized that Aaron was not. Aaron also lived in a damp hole in the earth somewhere in the bushes, and the air around him was always clammy. I liked him.

As Aaron disappeared behind Tiff, I felt the watchful presence of Hanna. I turned, and she was there smiling.

"I know something you don't," she said, the desire to be asked what that was, terribly unconcealed. She said things like this often, then studied your reaction. If you made the mistake of asking what it was she knew, the response was either, "Oh, nothing," or the answer was uninteresting and left you feeling lied to.

"What is it, Hanna?" Hunter said feebly, just to entertain her.

"I sink nobody knows zat Ezra lost a tooth!"

Isabelle sighed.

"Wow, fortunately we know now," Hunter said flatly.

All I could tell about Hanna was that she was German, liked to know everyone's business, and was uncannily present, especially when you sought privacy. She wanted to be part of everything, and often caused chaos, which was her delight.

"And I know something elseee!!!" she tried to lead us.

"I'm going to bed." Hunter declared, and we all eagerly agreed it was a good idea.

5

The weeks before the trimming activity began were lively and demanding. The farm was still quite underdeveloped and we scrambled to advance the infrastructure while the sun remained prominent in the sky.

Hunter and I spent a great deal of time building various structures from fir poles and canvas, or piecing together scrap wood for the less aesthetically demanding structures like the generator shed, which still powered the entire property. We ran countless electrical cables and water lines. We looked warily at the hoop houses and the dry rooms and hoped they would withstand the onslaught of the coming seasons. And on occasion, we rotated the collection barrels from the new and entirely unsavory composting toilet.

The land had improved, and continued to improve daily. It was amazing what many hands were capable of accomplishing in a short time. The transformation from raw land to a home for twenty-odd people, as it would be by the end of the season, was a testament to communal living. The plants were healthy and professional in their posture and prominence, which appropriately symbolized the state of the yearling farm. It began to feel as legitimate as a questionably legal farm can feel.

The season was already shifting—geese passing south and the land grown pale—but the days were still warm, the sun and the birds sang in harmony, and amidst the endless tasks, there were many festive and nude afternoons in the creek.

"Ah! I feel so free here!" Virginia declared.

There was a squeal of delight and we looked over towards Isabelle. She had just captured a toad and was looking pleased and awed by the utter amazement of everything in the universe. She was eternally in awe of the situation in which she found herself, and it reminded me not to forget how special these circumstances were. Many events in the greater world had aligned to allow for the existence of our farm and the other farms speckled across the west. Izzy was covered in turmeric from top to bottom, and looked like a woodland fairy crouched in the bushes. I stuck my tongue out at her and she beamed and squealed again.

"But what do you feel free from?" Hunter queried with grave curiosity. "By the way, you're in check, Benji."

We were playing naked chess out on the Triumph flood plain near a gurgling side channel. "I mean, I feel free too," Hunter continued, "but to feel that, shouldn't it be compared with something? Something that made you feel confined or restricted before?"

I looked at the huge sky, and at the unmarred wilderness around us. There were no humans in sight other than the cluster of youth I was among, youth who had stumbled into this freedom. All craving it, all speaking of it, but possibly not knowing what it was.

"I don't know, I guess," Virginia said with a pout.

Virginia was a friend of mine from Oregon, and had recently arrived with Pelli, the mother of Ezra, who was also a close friend from home. I experienced the sensation of freedom they were feeling too. When I discovered the farm culture of the Green Rush, I had just accepted that freedom, enjoyed it, basked in it, and avoided asking what it was that made it feel so liberating. There was nothing bad we were escaping, no wars, no devastating economic hardships, no oppression—but we were still seeking freedom.

"Goddammit, Hunter, quit chasing me around the board." I moved my King to another undesirable square.

"Well," Virginia started, "maybe we want freedom from judgment. I dunno. A lot of people here don't like what is happening in our society. They don't like expectations of how to live. They don't like the pressure to conform, to get a normal job and work until they are old. To work all the time, to have kids at the right time and to raise them in a certain way and educate them in a system that seems outdated. They don't like the media and the communication used. They don't like the way our politics work and the inequality and the influence of money. They aren't even sure if classic ideas of right and wrong are still valid. There are a lot of questions that are hard to ask in a system that is so set. A lot of people are unhappy, and there is an opportunity to try something different here without judgments and pressures."

Hunter looked amused. "That argument is full of holes. Maybe people don't like the standard societal structure, but are we really outside of it here? Everything is still about money. We still buy things, lots of things actually. We still support capitalism. We still use lots of the infrastructure from our country. We take advantage of all the things that help us—the roads, the machinery, the...."

"That doesn't matter!" Virginia interjected, showing her tendency towards passion. "I get it. We are privileged to be here. A lot of it is the stability and the fortune of living in a developed and wealthy country that allows us to have freedom from the things that we don't like. So shouldn't we take advantage of that? Use the things that serve us and discard the things that don't? Because that is what we are trying to figure out—what parts of our culture to keep, and what to throw out. This is an experiment that is allowed by the privilege of our country and our society so that our country and society can get better... even if they don't know it," she added with a smile. "We are social scientists, exploring new lifestyles from the context of what we know."

"Check." Hunter studied the chessboard. "Yes, we don't have to shun all of the system, that is true, and shouldn't because the old system allows us to make those changes. But it seems as if there are lots of transformations happening all over the place in the U.S., and in the world. Social ideas are changing everywhere, and not everyone is running away to make those transitions."

Virginia looked like she might become emotional, and Pelli stepped in to support her in her ever-practical way.

"Ok, yeah, sure, people are making changes," Pelli began, "but often their approach just leads to a fight or an endless argument that goes nowhere. Everyone has their own opinion and nothing ever happens because the debate gets in the way of action. Like Virginia just said, we have something like an experiment here. We don't have to listen to all the bullshit opinions while we are here. We just do things differently without fighting. When you change things according to society's rules, according to our current version of democracy, you just end up with endless discussion. That approach is just so fucking slow. Our technology and understanding of the world and how it works is accelerating, things around us are changing fast, but society is inching along. It's pretty damn close to stagnant. The changes aren't fast enough and I know that I believe humans can make huge changes much faster if we just *live* those changes and observe what works and what doesn't. Ok, it isn't perfect here because we aren't totally free, and we aren't totally clear on everything we want to change, but people aren't wasting time on conversations that are just slowing our evolution. I don't want to debate a woman's right to choose how to deal with a pregnancy. I don't want to hear about gay rights, or any other debate about personal freedoms. I don't want to hear a debate between a Democrat and a Republican because those are part of the same tired routine. Nobody here sees change in society the way they want to see it, or at the pace they know it could be in a world that changes so quickly. We want to see humans progress. It is exciting and we have potential, and here, we have a little more independence from stagnation and those bonds that don't let us move forward—from fear of change, I guess."

Pelli slammed her fist on the ground next to her and laughed at the spirited oratory she had just delivered.

"Well, that was eloquent, Pelli. You too, Virginia. I just wonder if everyone out there wants those fast-paced changes to go in the same direction you do." Hunter spoke like a professor encouraging his students.

"Well, of course not. But even if there isn't one common idea here, people are more likely to let one another pursue their own living experiment." Pelli laughed again. "I'm not gonna quit trying to make changes I believe in because someone disagrees. Then you come right back down to stagnation. Besides, our ideas are the right ones!" She winked at Hunter.

"Checkmate! Sorry, Benji, you play a terrible game of chess."

"Is that who I think it is?" Virginia jumped up in excitement.

A hobbit with curtains of hair to his waist was running naked across the savanna. He hobbled and hopped from time to time as he stepped on a sharp stone. He arrived winded and grinning.

"I heard there was naked chess by the river. Couldn't miss that! Can I play against Benji? He sucks."

I glared at my friend. "Hey, Cormac. Good to see you, old pal."

6

Working with friends from my home seemed to justify the

experience even more—I was validated by the presence of familiar people from my own small, simple community who also believed in the possibilities this lifestyle afforded. I felt this hidden paradise was expanding, drawing in more people, quietly influencing greater numbers, and affecting more distant communities. The presence of my childhood friends was notable, but the industry was drawing others in from much further abroad—people from around the world. There was an understanding that northern California and southern Oregon was a place where the global community could find a geographical holding.

Of course, there were still the locals.

The town of Tipsytom was really just half a town. It was built exclusively on one side of the road and all the buildings faced a large field on the other side. They seemed to regard the field as if it were a place to be feared. The town would not go to that side of the road.

It was an easy town to understand—the residents had no interest in complexity or excess. There was the general store that was also the single-pump gas station and the post office whenever the real post office was closed, which was six-and-a-half days a week. The store sold chips, soda, ice cream, beer, and beef jerky. It had a freezer full of locally butchered beef and pork, and inexplicably, organic soymilk. Next to the store was an abandoned commercial venue of unclear past, or future. Next to that was the dilapidated dwelling of an impoverished logging family. Next to that was a single-garage fire station. Next to that was an empty lot. And next to that was the post office, which, as I indicated, was open for one half-day every week, on Thursdays. That was the end of the town. The outskirts at the general store end of town hosted the community hall and McKitrick winery, which was just a warehouse. The outskirts on the post office end of town, right at the river bend, was Divinity Wind, the black sheep of the town, the lair of Raj Ras. But we weren't at that end of town.

Cormac and I had loaded the back of the truck with fourteen five-gallon gas cans, which we cycled through every four days to keep the generator running—the guilty wasteful side of the farm. We all grimaced when we boasted of the composting toilet and recalled that diesel still powered the entire property.

"We are a young farm. Solar is coming soon," Jona often defended.

We were filling the cans, and drinking 40s of malt liquor, and watching the local hillbillies. The pump was archaic and filling the fourteen cans took thirty-seven minutes, so there was always time to enjoy the local culture.

"Am I stereotyping if I call that guy a hillbilly?" I asked Cormac.

"Yes, you are. Am I stereotyping if I call the guy standing next to him a hillbilly?"

I nodded affirmative. The fellow I was inspecting was missing his front teeth, banging a can of chew in his palm, had a bulbous beer belly straining against his dirty tank top, and had purple flames tattooed the length of his arm. His companion was corpulent, wore long camouflage shorts and a Jacksonville Jaguars t-shirt with the sleeves cut off. He hid behind his wrap-around shades and was drinking Bush beer. Cormac shook with the silent uncontrollable laughter that made most people think he was in perpetual seizure.

"Can always spot a local."

Suddenly I saw a familiar personage emerge from the store.

"Henry!" I called. "Good to see you. Haven't been able to make it up to the bar yet to say hello."

"Ah, hey, Ben, nice to see you in the valley, but don't bother lookin for me at the bar." He made his way to the truck and pulled out a cigarette. "Sold it last spring."

"You sold the bar?"

"Yeeep. Sold it to try my hand growing weed for a living. Well that didn't fuckin pan out." He scowled at his fingernails, which were a rich shade of black.

"Shit man, what happened."

He looked baleful. "Turns out, I don't have a green thumb. Ah balls, put all my goddamn money into getting the plants up and going and they was all dead by August. Say, could I have a swig of that Old English?"

I handed him the bottle. "Damn, Henry, sorry to hear that. So what are you doing?"

He polished off the bottle with three hearty pulls. "Oh, I'm a trimmer now. Sparky put me to work. I ain't very good, but it's keepin me goin. But hell, I regret letting go of the Tipsy Tavern."

I nodded. "So who's runnin it? I saw it's still operating."

"Yeah, that would be Linda Feeny and her husband, Walter. New in town, nice folks. City folks from Colorado. Bought a house and Walter is growing for some fancy dispensary in San Francisco, and Linda runs the bar." He sighed long and audible.

"And those guys?" I asked, unable to deny my curiosity. "They must be locals huh?"

Henry glanced over his shoulder. "What, them two? Nah, they're new in the valley. Pot farmers like the rest of 'em, come out from somewhere back East." He spat. "It's all anyone does here anymore. Well, I don't own the bar, but I still go there. I think there's an open mic night this Thursday. See ya round."

We finished our fueling duties and headed back towards the farm.

"Well, that should teach us to stereotype," Cormac said.

7

The bar looked exactly the same, but felt subtly different. The rustic had an added touch of quaint, and they had one artisanal beer on tap. Linda was as sweet as candy and looked like Doris Day.

The local gang was more subdued and well behaved, and as people streamed in, I found I was having a harder time differentiating between locals and migrant marijuana workers. They were beginning to blend, assimilate to one another. Even after a year I could see this change and this made me feel both pleased and melancholy. It seemed that people were comfortable with one another, yet something was always lost when cultures blend—the story of a time and place was ending, and a new one was starting.

I had assumed our gang of ten or so would overwhelm the bar, but to my shock, people continued to flood through the doors. Trim season was underway and multitudes of immigrants were there and ready to become a participant of their chosen new home. The wilderness was transformed into a metropolis. The few locals I was sure of seemed to shrink down on their stools and focus on their drinks. Even Saucy Sally was shy in the crowd. What had these waves of foreigners who turned their remote valley into a center of activity done to their peaceful lives?

Hunter and I played the song, "Que Sera, Sera." We played it for Linda, but she didn't know it. Then I ate a hamburger. At least Jeff was still cooking the same burger. Cormac got drunk, and getting him home gave me an excuse to escape from the crowd. I was overwhelmed, too. A large population like that didn't make sense in that remote valley of contemplation and solitude.

Que sera, sera.

8

As the plants were harvested and the processing got underway, Jona decided that we should rebuild the cabin. His hands sat on his lap full of potential energy while we discussed the project. Jona's hands were often more active at rest than when they were engaged in a task. At rest, they were meditating on all possible actions, and the times they seemed to rest the most were the times when there was the most to do. Although it was hard to observe, those were the times when Jona accomplished remarkable things. I believe Jona's hands often made the decisions for him, and when there was a great deal of activity, they wanted more activity. Jona justified the needs of his poised hands in simpler terms.

"When the weather is good, prepare for winter."

So we dismantled all but one wall of the little home we had constructed in desperation the previous season, and set about expanding it into a new and far more permanent structure. On the second day, Cormac approached me and handed me a strip of leather about six inches wide and three feet long.

"You are gonna need this if we are gonna be building together."

"Is that so? Well, what is it?"

He grinned roguishly, his blond soul patch splashing from his bottom lip like an ornery wave. "Oh ho ho, he wants to know! This, my friend, is a loincloth. Until the weather changes, this is what we wear to work."

I had never imagined that a loincloth could be so comfortable. It allowed for maximum dexterity. Equipped with loincloth, boots, and tool belts, we set to work in earnest.

Cormac was a bit of everything, and as soon as you decided he was something, he changed because he didn't want to be whatever it was you wanted him to be. He was somewhere between a circus freak, hippy, redneck, Irishman, artist, soul singer, clown, philosopher, stoic, skeptic, cynic, believer, punk, romantic, thinker, feeler, good listener, bad listener, drug addict, Zen monk, and a drummer. But he was always a lover, and a laugher, and a good friend.

Cormac would read Zen koans in the morning, and then fart loudly when a female passed by. He would lecture on eating organic super foods, meditating, and the merits of shiatsu, then gripe about hippies while drinking cheap beer. He wore his red hair to his waist, often in braids, and clad himself in whatever vibrant garments he found at the thrift store... at least when he wasn't in a loincloth.

Though he was a number of years older than me, we had grown up in the same part of Oregon. We had worked together building theater sets in Eugene, and collaborated on art projects at festivals. The history of our friendship was comforting, but his best feature was that I could say anything without offending him. He actively undertook the task of breaking stereotypes, but he also loved identifying them.

Jona was busy rearing Ezra, and even busier entertaining the scores of women who were vying for him. He didn't like to leave the farm, so he would prepare elaborate lists of everything the farm needed, hook the trailer to his truck, hand us a paper bag full of cash, and send Cormac and me to Lassy.

"Ok, that lady?"

"Oh, man, don't make a joke of this. Burner, obviously! Don't you think I know my own kind?"

I scoffed. "All of them are your kind. What about him?"

He leaned forward. "Hillbilly. I thought it was a redneck for a minute, but it's a hillbilly." He broke into a fit of hysterical giggles.

We were sitting on the porch of the old cowboy saloon in Lassy drinking Whisky Gingers and stereotyping the traffic.

"What is the difference?"

Cormac swirled his whiskey and crossed his legs, playing the erudite role. "A hillbilly is someone who lives in rural areas. They are uneducated by dint of isolated geography. A redneck can live anywhere, and they are willfully ignorant."

I peered at the hillbilly plodding appropriately towards the feed store. "And how can you tell he is a hillbilly and not a redneck?"

Cormac chuckled in a knowing way. "The truck he just got out of doesn't have any Republican bumper stickers."

"Ah! I see. Well, does he grow pot?"

Cormac took one more thorough look as the defined hillbilly disappeared into the shop, stomping the mud from his boots at the door. "Yes."

"And how can you tell that?"

"I just can. Give me another."

I indicated a tall, slender man with dreadlocks walking up the main street.

"Rastafarian! Duh. He is wearing the colors—red, yellow, and green in a contiguous pattern, and of course the dreads."

"He is white, though!" I returned.

Cormac looked at me with repugnance. "Dude, a Rastafarian can be any color. It's a religion, not a race. But actually, to be a Rastafarian stereotype, they don't even have to know who Haile Selassie was. It's not really about religion anymore. The *only* requisites to being a Rastafarian are to have dreadlocks, listen to reggae, smoke weed, and wear some configuration of yellow, red, and green."

I groaned. "Well, I guess stereotypes don't have to involve reality. Does he grow pot?"

"Yes!"

I didn't ask how he knew. "Her?" I nodded.

"Oh! She's a redneck! Great example! And probably a meth addict. Look at her jaw grind away."

"Farmer?"

"Yep. Uhh... probably a trimmer in this case."

I grabbed his arm. "Black SUV. Just pulled up in front of the Mexican restaurant."

"Ah, I have been waiting for one of these guys to come along—Ball Capper. Probably from the Bay, was a hustler and decided to start farming. Still wears urban gear and a baseball hat pulled low, thus the name. Looks extremely out of place in a rural setting. Always drives an SUV or huge truck. Most easily identified weed farmer of them all."

I pointed at another.

"Hippy. Grows weed."

"Ok, well this is something I'm very interested in. What makes that person a hippy, as opposed to some other more specific stereotype?"

A sage smile spread across Cormac's gnomish face. "Ah, my little grasshopper. You are learning. Yes, the term hippy is an umbrella stereotype we use when no other prominent traits allow for a more precise pigeonhole. *Hippy* is actually so ambiguous that it is just a way of saying *I know nothing about that person, but they dress in a way that indicates they have a set of values that society would consider 'liberal.'* Redneck is almost its counterpart."

Cormac pointed at Capricorn Café. "There's a hippy, there's another, there's another. They don't look anything alike, but you wouldn't classify them as rednecks. Fewer labels on their clothes, slightly harrier, that's all. Now that guy though, he is New Age!"

We watched a lean man with a shaved head and straight spine walk into Gaia. He wore a loose shirt of natural fibers with no collar and long loose sleeves, and white linen pants.

"That guy is buying coconut oil and chia seeds. Then he is going to his home that has no chairs to listen to hang drum music and hold a crystal for the next fifteen hours." We both burst into laughter.

"And you can tell this by looking, huh?"

"Benji, that's what you do when you stereotype. You determine who somebody is and what they do based on their appearance. Of course that guys is doing all of those things, and when he is done squeezing quartz, he is going to float in a sensory deprivation tank and astral project into hyper-intelligent dimensions."

"Seems like an interesting guy. I imagine he grows pot?"

Cormac was thoughtful. "Actually no, he doesn't."

I sensed a punch line building. "Go ahead. Get it over with, Mac!"

He giggled "He doesn't grow it... he lets it grow!"

I rolled my eyes.

We identified a back-to-the-lander wearing a mixture of gardening apparel and homemade garments. Back-to-the-landers were in the area to practice primitive skills, sustain themselves from their environment, and make this process a bit more comfortable by growing pot. We saw several Burners who were dressed in burlesque and circus costumes, or had top hats with goggles strapped to them, or had geometric patterns shaved into one side of their scalp and long hair on the other. They were there to grow weed through the sunny months and fund their festival addiction. There was a cluster of twenty-somethings wearing shredded black jeans and vests with patches and spiky metal ornamentation.

Cormac defined them as Gutter Punks, and elaborated on their habits, explaining that they were middleclass youth who had general contempt for anyone who worked, and asked people who worked to give them money. He felt confident that they were there to try trimming, but would almost certainly quit when they discovered that trimming was a form of work.

"And those two in tight pants—everyone knows that one," Cormac said as we worked through another whiskey. "Hipsters! Just people who wear mainstream fashion. Your average person despises them, and your average person *is* them. And yes, they are growing weed."

I watched the diversity of people mill about the town—a clash of cultures and the blending of cultures simultaneously. There were many different backgrounds, personas, and looks, but they were all in Northern California for the same reason. "They all grow pot."

Cormac nodded. "Yep. And they are all just people. No different from you or me."

I smirked. "I dunno, what about that guy? What is he?" A man with short hair, in blue jeans and a t-shirt, walked past us on the sidewalk.

Cormac watched him until he passed behind a building. "He's an alien. But he still grows weed."

We bumped our way back along the gravel road to Tipsytom, winding around the corkscrew bends with an overburdened truck and trailer. We had most of the makings for a house with us, and a few groceries. We were still dissecting the community, but we had moved on to interactions.

"The thing is, they so often break any stereotypes you want to put on them. That's why I just think of everyone out here as an individual within the same subculture. Once we arrive in this place, it doesn't matter what you came from. Here, first and foremost, we are all farm workers. We just happen to be wearing different clothing."

I took a graceful curve between a passing logging truck and an unwelcome plunge into the ravine. I watched a small sliver of the road crumble away in the rearview mirror. It tumbled silently into the abyss. The wheels rubbed against the wells and screamed out a reminder that we had a bed full of plywood and concrete and a trailer piled with lumber.

"Go on," I said.

"Well, out here where there isn't a great deal of infrastructure, and the chances of things going amiss are high, and you need to be on good terms with your neighbors, all of the things that separate us kind of seem unimportant. At that point, the person who you had categorized and labeled is just an individual. In that case, people are going to shatter stereotypes all the time. The peaceful hippy from whom you expect clarity and support might turn out to be a dickhead and a complete imbecile because those people are in every demographic. And the gangster you think is shady and might rip you off is going to give you the shirt off of his back, and bake you a cake, and pull you out of your burning house because he is a good person. Doesn't matter that one has dreads and one wears an Oakland Raiders hat pulled down over his eyes."

I edged us around a rockslide and the trailer stuttered sideways, moving us towards the drop once again. I gently accelerated to encourage our survival.

"You see, it's all about navigation," Cormac explicated. "We are all in the same situation, which makes us part of the same culture. But because we come from such varied backgrounds, we all have different ways of communicating. The key in this culture, whether you are a hillbilly, or a Rastafarian, or a hipster, is to learn how to communicate with people on their level, using their language. We have to realize that we all have our own vernacular and our own definitions of the words we use."

I nudged the breaks as a deer bolted across the road. "Like, you may say *tribe*, whereas I might say *community*, and be speaking about the same thing. Or I say *energy*, referring to the force moving this frightening vehicle along this frightening road, and you might use energy to talk about spirituality. Things like that?"

"Yes! Exactly that. We have to listen to the words and listen beyond them and hear what someone is trying to communicate."

The brakes were working only marginally, and so I drifted down the middle of the road heading down the final slope into Tipsytom, hoping that no cars were coming from the other way. Because there would be no communicating of any kind in any language.

"So, I have to endure people talking about chakras and the divine feminine?"

Cormac giggled in spite of his apparent fear of my driving. "Yep, Ben, listen to the people even if it is just a bunch of hippy bullshit!"

9

I was drinking tea and watching the mist rise from the valley. Isabelle was sitting in the morning meditation circle that took place every day on the deck of the unfinished cabin. Isabelle looked around and smiled, then got up and came over. She looked happy but a bit perturbed.

"It was kind of weird. Hanna told me last night that you are in love with her."

I spit my tea onto the earth in alarm. "She said what? That girl is fucking nuts and fucking manipulative."

Izzy snickered, "Well I thought she was just being Hanna, but I wasn't sure."

Later that day I was up on the hillside working on a burst water line when Hanna appeared unexpectedly right behind me.

"Oh god! Hanna, how did you get up here without me noticing? Jeezus, you scared me. Stealthy girl!"

She looked sly. "I just come to you because I can trust you. You listen. I sink Mara is trying to steal Jona from me. She is a bit crazy, you know?" Hanna wandered around picking at blades of grass, nonchalant and smiling, humming to herself. "If these bitches keep trying to get in my way..." she shrugged and beamed at me, "I might get angry! Hahaha!" She laughed lightly and my skin crawled.

"Hanna, I have to be honest. Jona has any number of lovers, and I know emotions are difficult, but this is a work environment and it needs to function smoothly for the whole community. We have a lot of people here now, and interpersonal drama isn't going to help anything, so just focus on yourself and you might want to accept that you may not get Jona to yourself."

Hanna glared at me. "You are not so nice, you know?"

I sighed. "Hanna, you told Izzy that I'm in love with you. Why did you do that? It's a lie, and I think you said it to hurt her. I'm just being straightforward with you because you are sowing tension."

She looked at me blankly. then turned and began to skip carelessly down the hill. She called over her shoulder in a singsong voice, "You are in love with me! And Isabelle told me she doesn't love you!"

I don't have time for this shit, I thought. And I didn't. We had twenty-three people living on the farm by then.

Laughter and smiles were the predominant offerings from the community that had come together from the far appendages of the planet. I was always thankful for that attitude because the land was put under a great deal of stress accommodating that many bodies. The smiles were my quiet signal that everyone was getting what they needed. But even with motivated and self-empowered individuals, some came with a princess complex, or heavy emotional burdens that they dragged along to share with the group.

Jona and I watched them come, alone or in pairs. We were delighted and nervous.

"Jona, I love women, don't get me wrong, but... it's all women."

He smiled at me sheepishly. "I have a weakness, Benji."

I regarded the mountain man, one of the most capable men I had ever met. He was hard as stone on the outside, but all honey and goose feathers on the inside.

I put a hand on his shoulder. "Just be prepared, we are putting fifteen women together in a yurt for an entire month. There will be some blood."

Half the women were Latinas from Mexico, Puerto Rico, Colombia, Chile, Argentina, and Uruguay. There was also our clan from Oregon, and some Californians. One male, Mason, came with his partner, took one look at the situation, and kept his head down. There were also the Germanic folk, and the Floridians working the land, and Hunter from Iowa. We were a community, an international one, and everyone was doing their best to be a part of the group and to offer their individual strengths to create stability for the whole. It was the closest representation of a commune I'd ever seen, although knowing it was temporary made it more exciting and more achievable to everyone there. We were there to participate in a social experiment, and each of us had a role. For that moment in time, above everything else in our lives outside the Tipsytom, we were a tribe.

Book Three

Part 2

1

Aaron moved out and that was the beginning of bedlam.

I hadn't really considered that someone could move off of the land and still work there. It just seemed so out of character for the community, but I helped Aaron load his belongings into Helga. As we were preparing to leave, Hanna skipped up.

"I think I vill come and help with the move!"

I looked at Aaron who displayed an absurd degree of enthusiasm "Yeeeeeaaahh! This is all I could have hoped for! A moving party with... Hannaaaaa! K let's go!"

Hanna missed the sarcasm, and we rumbled up the driveway towards the village of Tipsytom.

"So I sink I'm in love with you, Benji!"

I groaned. "No you aren't, Hanna."

Aaron clapped his hands. "That's great, Hanna! I'm in love with Benji too!"

How did I get stuck with the two lunatics, I thought. "C'mon, Aaron, leave her alone."

He looked offended. His pallid face loomed near me and he leaned over. "It's true. I am in love with you. It's one of the reasons I'm leaving. I can't be around you. That and the fact that I can't handle all the hippies running around waving eagle feathers and doing their yoga and chanting in the kitchen when I'm trying to make my coffee. But yes, I am in love with you."

I was puzzled, so I drove faster. I wanted to finish this errand quickly.

"So, you're both in love with me. Hanna, I thought you were in love with Jona. And Aaron, I didn't know you were gay."

Aaron chuckled.

Hanna uttered some strange nonsense about a wishing well, and that the geese flying south were whispering messages to her.

Aaron chuckled again and I increased my speed a bit more.

"Gay, straight, man, woman! I don't even know what those are! I'm a pan-sexual," said Aaron. "I could be sexually attracted to anything, if the energy is erotically enticing."

"Anysink?" Hanna asked in Germanic amazement.

"Yes, any *sink* Hanna... if it is erotically enticing. Or other inanimate objects, but lalalala, I prefer the animate most of the time." He reached over and pinched my cheek.

I realized that Aaron's eccentric personality had just been a cover for an even more eccentric personality cowering and giggling beneath. And now that he had extricated himself from the space where he felt constrained, he was revealing it... to me! Fortunately, Hanna demanded attention at that moment.

"The women here are all snakes!"

I looked at Hanna in the rearview mirror. She was smiling her benign little smile, and nodded at me. She didn't blink. "You know what the snake does? It spreads poison. I know how to catch the snakes though! I am a snake charmer you see!"

Aaron was watching me with delight. "No! give *me* your attention, Benjamin! Give it to me!" he cooed.

"Oh look, guys! We are at Divinity Wind! Aren't we all so happy that it was a short drive!"

A very pale white man with a receding hairline backed by red curls was standing at the entrance to Divinity Wind. He was wearing flowing white garments. He smiled with intentional pain. "Welcome, friends! I'm Suman, a *friend* of Raj Ras. He is waiting for you in the sanctuary."

Divinity Wind was the least appropriate installment one could possibly inflict upon Tipsytom, and everything about it was incompatible. Most people in town simply pretended it didn't exist. Divinity Wind was the strange child that looked almost normal, but clearly wasn't. Everyone was slightly afraid of it, and hoped it would just go away. It was a UFO that had audaciously landed on the edge of town and decided it liked the climate.

Divinity Wind began its existence with a normal motel name like *The Tipsytom Motel*, or some such adequately dull title. It had been built in the early seventies as a mundane motel and campground. When it transitioned to its new life as Divinity Wind, it became confused about its identity and unsure how to look the part. Divinity Wind now looked exactly as it always had, but run down, neglected and ornamented with prayer flags hanging in the trees and stone sculptures of meditating deities in the yard.

The place had the classic layout of a drive-up motel with a gravel parking lot in front of a crude wooden fence. There was a comfortably large grass yard with a few alder trees, and one long, single-storey building with six separate entrances to six identical rooms. There were two small outbuildings, and a much older house on the property, which had been occupied by the previous owners. The house looked moldy on the outside, and it turned out to be dark and moldy on the inside. This was Aaron's new home, and it was fitting.

Divinity Wind was no longer a motel. It was an incense factory and smelled of one thousand ornately, extravagantly, dead plants. The force field of smell protected the dumpy, little, fading red motel with its chipped paint and slumped gutters. I wondered if ill wishers would reach the gate and find themselves under such omnipresent olfactory siege that they would immediately lose their mind, stuff dirt into their nostrils and flee.

Aside from Aaron's new abode, which was unusable for anything other than accommodations for someone just like Aaron, there were two other buildings where the incense was produced. I assumed people worked there, but no one was ever seen. It was a place where one felt a presence rather than saw a person. I peered through the partially open door as we passed. There was a great deal of clanking from machines, and steam rising, but no people.

Suman gingerly led us silently along the external concrete corridor. Room number 3 was the sanctuary.

Raj Ras was kneeling at his altar on the mangy carpet. He was preparing ayahuasca and swaying to the sounds of sitar and chimes skittering from a small, obscured speaker tucked into a potted plant. There was nothing in the room other than the altar and the potted plant. Paint was lazily peeling from the walls, and the sixty-watt bulb was unconcealed by any fixture. Raj Ras did not turn when we entered. He finished his task, said a prayer to the framed portrait of a bearded man, and finally lit a coal and placed it in the censer.

"We have hinoki cypress today," he said silkily, and ran his long fingers through his hair. His mullet was gray—the kind of gray that suggested an enchantment of old age had been cast upon him, rather than the gray due to traditional decay brought on by time. His tunic was plain and white. Finally, Raj Ras turned and beheld us, studying our auras, calmly, without judgment.

"Please, have a seat. Would you like some ayahuasca? We won't have the ceremony until tomorrow, but if it calls you to partake then it is best to acknowledge the spirit's message."

"I can't at the moment, Raj," I said. "Thanks, though. I'm just here to drop off Aaron, and Isabelle asked me to buy some incense."

"Oh yeah! Sure, Suman can organize anything you need. If she wants to buy ten packages I can offer a fifteen percent discount." His voice remained even and soothing. North American gurus were ever the astute businessmen.

Raj Ras looked at the others with pellucid blue eyes. "Are either of you interested in medicine at the moment?"

"She wants sandalwood and that guggul-amber combination. *Sorry!*" I finished in a hushed tone, suddenly aware that my volume had disrupted the ambiance.

"Oh, that's quite all right. We value the sounds of celebration here." His smile was forgiving. "I can offer all the sandalwood she can manage, but I have only three packs of guggul at the moment. It's very popular and we are selling it as fast as we can make it!"

Suman emitted a choked noise from the corner where he stood silently. It might have been a giggle.

Raj Ras stared at Suman, his face impassive and clearly admonishing. He lifted an eagle feather from the altar. "And she is aware that the price is somewhat higher for the guggul?"

"Yeah, she has been studying the price sheet you brought over last week. She sent me with a precise order. I think she wants five guggul, but I'll surprise her with some of this....?"

"Mmm, hinoki cypress! Yes, it's very pleasant, isn't it?"

Raj Ras sounded like a purring cat. "And... it's our sale product this week, so if you buy ten packs of hinoki, I can offer you a twenty percent discount... and since you're a friend, let's just make it twenty-five!"

I saw Hanna eying the bottle of murky liquid on the tray next to Raj Ras.

"Well, I don't think I need... yeah, ok. Hanna, you don't need that right now. Let's unload Aaron and get back to the farm."

Raj laughed in a high and pointedly clear voice. "You are all welcome here anytime for a Santo Daime ceremony. We are having a gathering tomorrow night, for the full moon! Benjamin, I've been expecting you to come at some point."

I smiled. "I will, when we have a slow moment on the land."

"Suman, could you organize the transaction with Benjamin, and show Aaron to his accommodations? Welcome Aaron!"

Raj Ras turned back to his altar.

"I like that guy," I announced while Hanna and I drove back to the farm.

"So, he is some kind of shaman? I only hear rumors about him."

"Yeah," a chuckle fought its way out. "Some call him that. I suppose a shaman gives you something, and people always seem to leave Divinity Wind with something." I patted the bag of incense.

Hanna lost her mind the following evening.

2

The moon was full and the second road kill of the season had been butchered, burnt, and eaten. We were suffering through the intense heat and duration of a ceremonial sweat.

Fifteen of us were shoulder-to-shoulder, cross-legged in a turtle shell structure made from woven willow and covered with blankets and canvas. Tiffany had smudged us one by one with a smoldering bundle of sage and an eagle feather, and we had crawled through a flap into the darkness, pawing our way counter-clockwise around the empty fire pit until we reached the person in front. Then, using a pair of elk antlers, Tiffany delivered the glowing rocks that had been basking in a bonfire all afternoon. They were special volcanic rocks brought from the slopes of Mt. Shasta. Tiffany passed the rocks to Jona, who praised them for their heat and appreciable age, and placed them in the pit. After the rocks had been nested, Tiffany joined us and the glowing orange pile began to express its potential, filling the enclosure with waves of heat. Jona splashed water on the rocks and dropped a cedar sprig onto them.

It was my first ceremonial sweat, and only moments in my crossed legs ached and thick beads of sweat surfaced on my skin. I wasn't sure I could endure the multiple hours that Jona had solemnly predicted the sweat lodge ceremony would last.

"To the east, we give thanks!" Jona's rich voice defeated the silence. He followed a procedure based on the traditions of the indigenous Northern Californians, but admitted to using a fusion of various practices and wouldn't claim authenticity.

"To the east, where the sun rises and earth is refreshed, the Earth Mother provides. To the south, we give thanks. To the south, the fire, passion, mmm, yes, thank you for the fire! And to family."

Several people murmured the word, "Aho," an expression of agreement.

"To the west! The water, the feeling, we give thanks to the west, and to our individual spirits! And to the north, the wind, the land of the ancestors we give thanks for teaching us how to be, and to exist in harmony, for the wisdom you share."

Jona lapsed into silence. I heard a number of deep breaths. The air around my body was inescapable heat, and the liquid within me coursed out in a futile attempt to cool the assailing fever.

The first round belonged to the ancestors. All present had the opportunity to speak at length regarding their thoughts and gratitude on this topic. Through the growing delirium, we passed our words and songs and chants around the circle until finally, the speaking feather returned to Jona. He reiterated many thanks to the wind and to the ancestors, and then feigning patience, we all slowly crawled from the oppression and the enlightenment to fling ourselves with desperation into the creek. The steam burst from our skin, sending plumes of vapor towards the beaming moon high above. Gasping and laughing we lay in the sand on the beach.

And too soon, Jona announced it was time for the second round. *How long had the first been? An hour at least!* And now another round; this time to celebrate the earth.

In the maddening heat of the second session, somewhere in the middle, after many "Ahos" had already been moaned and mumbled, and many of us had shifted to our knees to rub our heads in the dirt, smear our bodies with mud made by our own sweat, and grovel before the eternal embers, Hanna received the eagle feather and spoke.

"Ah yes, the earth! Yes, it is nice, but I sink I want to talk about some people who don't understand what they are doing, what they are feeling."

A sudden heaviness formed in the demanding heat and fomented imminent disaster. Hanna's voice trotted along in the darkness with melodic ease. "This man wants to go back to the mother of his child, but this is a bad idea because he doesn't understand zat he is in love with me."

Oh god, here we go, I thought.

And then she stopped. "Zat is all."

The feather was passed and I breathed a sigh of relief. Ines, the Colombian, began to speak and the tension eased. I let my mind wander into the depths, and I watched the visions brought on by the remote words. I saw sheaves of golden wheat stretching to expansive distance, and deer the size of elephants. I saw Jona with a bow stalking one of the mighty deer, crouched, and watching it. I looked back at the deer, but where it had been standing, alert and regal, now there was a bed, and in that bed was Hanna with an infant suckling her breast. She had many arms and they were all reaching towards Jona.

"Hanna!"

I was recalled to the surface.

"Hanna! You need to calm down! Ines is holding the eagle feather. You spoke, now it is time to listen." Jona's voice, though even, was a scarce cover for the building distress.

Hanna didn't seem to hear him. She prattled on softly, becoming more detailed in her suspicions, accusations, and fantasies. Her sentences trailed off and regrouped into new thoughts before the prior one had finished.

"Hanna, this is a space for everyone to share. If you don't respect the rules of the ceremony, I will have to ask you to leave!"

Hanna ignored, or possibly, didn't hear Jona, and continued uttering her visions that swam enticingly around the circle-like siren dreams, painting scenes, hypnotizing our delirious minds, her soft tone cutting through Jona's louder more forceful voice with the brutal violence of sweetness.

"Yes, I sink I vill leave. But you vill regret this!"

Hanna suddenly gasped, as if she had just awakened to find that she was tangled in a blanket and couldn't breathe. "Air!!" she croaked "I need air!"

Dark bodies hurriedly compacted to make way for the clawing shadow reaching for the door to the east, groping for the earth and the rising sun.

We were silent when we exited the lodge the second time and we bathed in the creek in pensive contemplation. Jona insisted we continue with the ceremony. "This is a form of medicine and we will all find our different approach."

Hanna is losing it, not healing, I thought.

Hanna returned during the next session as we were speaking about family and the ones we loved. She spoke through the walls in a humble voice, asking to be invited back. Jona, understanding that everyone struggles, allowed her to return. "But if you leave again, Hanna, or speak out of turn, or direct negative words towards someone in the circle, you won't be invited back."

The atmosphere seemed surreal. My body had turned to liquid, and the pain in my hips, knees, and ankles was consuming me. Words came and went on their own, and the visions did the same. The only constant was the scent of cedar and the steady glow of the volcanic stones. And then Hanna's voice returned with alarming force.

Hanna suddenly shrieked, "Men are liars! They sink they can choose who they vant! But I choose who *I* vant!" Her voice shattered the world. She scrambled through the tent flap and the rest of us sat stupefied.

The final round was largely silent. Nobody seemed sure we were still profiting from the experience. Jona was intent to finish, and I understood that he needed it for himself. The weight of Hanna's suffering was tied to him, and though her reactions were outside the bounds of his understanding or obligation, the responsibility was his. I sat for him, but the feather moved quickly, and only Jona spoke at length, emphasizing emotional fortitude, patience, and compassion. He needn't have spoken indirectly. We all knew.

The moon was disappearing over Rolltop Ridge. I dove into the creek and then made my way towards the yurt. I wanted to talk with Isabelle about the events of the night. Virginia was pacing the room, teary eyed, and Pelli was reasoning with her. Ana and Flor, the Mexican and Chilean, were sitting at the trimming table distractedly snipping at buds, smiles far away.

"What's up, Virginia? You ok?"

Virginia ran over and hugged me and wiped her tears on my shirt.

"Oh, Ben, Hanna came in here, and she was totally crazy and screaming and just saying all of this nonsense, and she accused us of trying to destroy her. I don't know what she was talking about, it was total gibberish. And she screamed in my face, and then ran around grabbing things and throwing them on the floor. She was opening everyone's bags and pulling stuff out and throwing it."

I looked around and saw that the yurt was a bit more of a mess than usual, although it always looked like a poorly organized wardrobe.

"Fuck! And where is she now? Do I need to find her?"

Virginia sank into a chair. "No, Aaron came in when she was throwing things and he managed to calm her down a little and he took her to see Raj Ras. Oh, he took your car. Hanna is crazy, like totally gone."

I nodded. "Don't worry, it will be ok."

But then the rains came.

3

It was three in the morning and I was on the half-finished roof of the cabin with Jona, spreading tarps.

"Where the hell did the rain come from?"

I said this not to Jona but to the sky. I had fallen asleep two hours earlier under a sky sprayed with stars, happy to forget the agitations of the night, and now water was pouring to earth as though quenching a parched throat.

Cormac yelled from below, "Major problem! The dry rooms are flooding and the roofs on all of them are trapping water."

Moments later, Hunter appeared. His headlight was a bobbing, darting eye in the night. "Not good, guys. The electrical splitter melted. We can run only the dry rooms, or the kitchen, or the yurt."

Jona grabbed his beard with exasperation. "Gotta be the plants. Let's get off this fucking roof and get the water off the dry rooms."

I knew what the rains meant from the previous year— everything is great and in perfect order until the rains come. And then everything is terrible. The chaos of Viet-tom had returned.

The next three days were the sleepless routine I expected. The population of the farm spent the mornings huddled around the woodstove in the kitchen, watching the fire pit turn into a lake, and watching the dry patch of dirt that defined the kitchen floor shrink as the saturated ground outside began to consume the spaces under cover. We built wooden plank causeways between the kitchen and the yurt, spanning the perfidious mud pits that had formed as soon as the rain started, and would remain until spring. We affectionately called it *The Pits*.

I spent the days in the dry rooms in a nest of bailing wire and fan cables, emptying the dehumidifiers, pushing water off the tarp roofs, keeping constant vigilance on the state of the generator, and fighting off flashbacks from Viet-tom. Each night I battled my way across the beach, which had become a torrent of water, and climb out of my saturated clothes knowing that sleep would be short lived. I was already awake at two, or three, or four, when Jona would yell for assistance and I would don my mud-splattered raingear and slog up the hill to dig trenches in the mud outside the dry rooms, the yurt, and the kitchen with the futile aim of redirecting the relentless water.

"The rain can't last much longer," Jona said plaintively as we made an emergency run to Lassy for straw and propane, and for a sparkplug for the generator. "It hasn't let up for three days."

The hardware store was out of tarps, and everything else useful. Distraught farmers peeled through town with panic ingrained on their faces. Rain was a big deal in farm country, especially where there were so many underdeveloped, fledgling farms. The feed store was out of straw. Michael and Joe were buying birdfeeders, which were not, at that moment, desperately in demand. They were both relaxed and pleasant, and Jona and I both glowered in spite of ourselves.

"Yeah, people are saying there is a curse on this county. It's dry in the rest of the state," Joe noted in neighborly commiseration. "But Michael has everything buttoned down, so we are weathering things all right. Thanks for asking!"

We hadn't asked.

"It does feel like a curse," Jona admitted as we tore back to the farm dangerously undersupplied. "First Hanna goes bat-shit crazy. By the way, we hooked up only once, and I told her very clearly that I have other partners. Besides, I kind of thought she liked you."

I pointed out the rockslide that had overtaken a good share of the road, and Jona wheeled around it. He drove vehicles like he was riding a horse bareback. Men like Jona had to deal with technology as if it was a wild animal, otherwise it would not work for them.

"Now the rains are trying to wash us out of the valley! Well, it doesn't matter, I guess. Curse or no, the rains will do what they do, and I think Hanna was gonna lose it one way or another. Should have seen it coming." Jona accelerated down the river that had once been a road, and we slid dangerously close to the precipice.

"Why does driving this road always feel like an allegory?" I asked, but Jona didn't hear.

"Yep, should have seen it coming. Well, I have a feeling things are going to calm down soon."

Then Cormac nearly died.

4

A girl cried out from the yurt. By the time I arrived, others were crowding in. Virginia was in tears again. A group around the couch were exclaiming and talking all at once.

"Oh my god! What happened?"

"Shit, do we need to get him to a hospital?"

"Shut up, guys, let him talk!"

"Cormac, what happened?"

Someone shifted and I saw Cormac. His face was covered in blood. There was at least one laceration above his eye, but it was hard to tell if there were others because the congealed blood was so ubiquitous. I walked over and joined the group.

Cormac looked at the congregation and tried to smile, but winced instead. "Uh, I hurt pretty bad. What happened?"

We looked at one another.

"We don't know what happened, Cormac, we were hoping you did," Hunter said, chuckling nervously.

Cormac looked around, and back at us. "What am I doing in the yurt?"

Virginia choked back a sob.

"He has a concussion," Pelli said.

Hunter leaned in and looked at the cut above Cormac's eye. "He has another cut by his hairline. You found him, Virginia?"

She nodded. "I came in and he was just asleep here on the couch and I saw his face...."

Cormac smiled and winced again, then reached up to his face. "Oh man, I'm bleeding," he said as he regarded his sticky, red fingertips. "And my body really hurts. What happened?"

Hunter looked at me again. "We don't know, Macky, but we will figure it out."

At that moment, Flor entered with warm water and a cloth, and the first aid kit. Cormac smiled mischievously as the women began to fuss over him. "Maybe I should get busted up more often."

Virginia touched his side and he lurched in pain, and then lurched again because lurching had caused more pain. "Well, I think my ribs are fucked up, and my hip," he groaned through clenched teeth.

Pelli forced everyone back. "If he got hit by a car or something, his spine could be damaged. Cormac, listen to me. Do you feel any tingling anywhere? Or any pain in your back or neck?"

He regarded her for a moment, his mouth slack, then seemed to absorb her words. He looked confused. "Noo, no, I don't think so. No tingling. My whole body hurts, but I don't think it's my back."

We all exhaled our relief.

"Cormac, can you tell me the last thing you remember?"

Hunter said, looking directly into Cormac's eyes to get his attention.

Cormac stared at him blankly. "I... was at the tavern... I remember going up there in the evening because I needed a drink... yep, that's it." He beamed at Hunter like a proud child and then settled back with a sigh while the girls scrubbed the blood from his face and inspected him for other injuries.

Hunter and I stepped out of the yurt into the miserably wet daylight and tugged at our beards, a universal indicator of males immersed in grave thought.

"Do we need to get him to a hospital? Because that is at least three hours away. We don't really know how bad his injuries are."

Hunter assaulted his neon orange facial hair. "What the hell happened to him, Benji? Did he get in a bar fight? Did he get hit by a car? He has no recollection. Is it because he was drunk or because he has a bad concussion? Or both?"

I yanked at my beard and kicked a clump of mud. "He does black out when he drinks. I've seen that often enough. But he isn't a fighter. No, he's a pretty peaceful, happy drunk."

Hunter held a fistful of his beard and, for additional support, grabbed the hair of his scalp as the circuits in his mind whizzed and clinked in overdrive. "He seems to think his back and neck are all right, and his motions seemed ok until he discovered his ribs... I don't want to make the trip to the hospital until we get a better grasp on his injuries. The cuts on his face are bloody, but they are superficial, they don't need stitches. He may have some busted ribs, and we don't know how bad his hip is... Fuck."

I wrenched at my beard and had an idea. "Let's go to the bar. Linda might know."

We tore up the hill, slipping and scrambling through the mud.

"He was in here, sure. There weren't many last night. Folks are pretty busy on their farms dealing with the water these days."

We had decided that beer would help us think while we talked to Linda. She had served him ample drinks, and he had left without altercation.

"He certainly had a few. Are you guys trying to make your beards grow by yanking on them like that? Golly! Just drink your beer."

I laughed. "This sweetheart just said *golly*."

She rolled her eyes. "Finish your beers and go back to work."

We walked back along the road wondering if we would find some evidence, but there was none.

"If he had been hit by a car, the person would have stopped. I can't imagine a hit and run on a dark, stormy night. The valley is too small for that behavior."

We even tried to identify his boot marks in the mud, but then we realized we were buzzed from the beers and had no idea what his boot prints looked like.

Cormac was making his way to the kitchen when we returned. Virginia was under one arm and Ana under the other.

"He is speaking clearly. His head hurts, and he definitely has a concussion, but it isn't bad."

Cormac turned to us slowly with a meek smile. "But I still don't have a fucking clue what happened. And my ribs are fucked, and I can't put any pressure on my left leg."

Hunter's hand strayed towards his beard, but he caught it. "We went to the bar. You didn't get in a fight, and we are pretty sure you didn't get hit by a car. So we think you fell."

Although we searched the property, we couldn't find any signs of a fall, or the scene of a disaster. Cormac refused to go to the hospital, so I made him crutches from an ash tree we were turning into firewood. He hung up his loincloth for the season and joined the gals in the yurt to trim, sitting on the couch with his leg up, and reveling in the attention from the females.

Fuck You! I mouthed to him silently as I tromped out into the rain to work. He winked.

I wanted to get another stretch of sheeting on the roof. We needed the dry space, and the rain still showed no sign of abating.

On the roof, right near the apex, I found a hat and rolling tobacco. It was Cormac's. A little further down the slope was a lighter, and right next to the edge was a wet, but neatly rolled cigarette. I scooted to the precipice and looked down. Bellow was a telltale depression in the mud. On all sides of the depression, rebar was sticking out of the ground like fangs.

"You were drunk, and you passed out on the roof and rolled off."

I handed him his tobacco and hat. Cormac looked at them, then at me.

"And you are really fucking lucky. If you had fallen anywhere else, you would have been impaled by the rebar stakes we pounded for those guy lines."

I wanted to be angry with Cormac for being irresponsible. We were far from any medical assistance, and the farm was full of accidents waiting to happen. But, I was a reckless youth myself. And my thoughts of a good scolding were banished in that moment because Hanna returned.

My hand went to my beard.

5

Aaron seemed to find it all very amusing and marched down the drive as though he had discovered a unicorn and was parading it before the public. Hanna didn't have much to say. She floated down the path, impervious to the mud and wrapped in white sheets.

"She needs a few things," Aaron told Jona, who became agitated by her presence.

"Ok, but I think it is better if she doesn't stay. People are a little uncomfortable with her right now and we have a lot of work to focus on."

Jona looked at Hanna for a moment. She wore her eternal Mona Lisa smile, but rather than her usual watchful eyes, she had a glossed-over expression.

"Is she ok?"

Aaron breathed deeply with perverse relish. "Ooh, yes! She is great! She thinks she is Cleopatra. Raj gave her ayahuasca, and she took her clothes off and danced in front of a mirror for five hours. She is perfectly happy!" Aaron clapped his hands together and squeezed a loathsome smile onto his face.

Jona ignored his sarcasm. "Why did he give her ayahuasca?"

Aaron's smile broadened. "Raj let's people make their own decisions, and he says that the spirit of the ayahuasca always has the right answers."

Jona, who probably would have agreed with this most of the time, was unsure what to say. "Ok, can she stay with you guys for a couple more days? I don't think she should stay in the valley. Maybe we need to get her back to Germany."

Hanna spoke for the first time. "No, I don't sink I want to go to Germany, I sink I vill stay here."

Jona pulled on his beard, and I realized I was doing the same.

"Ok, Aaron," Jona said, "try to figure out if she knows people in the area. She can't stay on the land. I feel a lot of bad energy. I can take her to Arcata in a few days, on Halloween weekend. I am taking Ezra to go trick-or-treating and to see some friends."

Hanna was swaying gently from side to side. Her presence was causing Jona overwhelming distress. I had never seen him so uncertain. Even the gruffest of mountain men could be defeated by the wiles of romance.

Aaron bowed with absurd dramatization. "As you wish." He spun on his heels. "Come, Hanna! Let's go back to your kingdom."

Hanna floated out behind him trailing her muddy sheets. "Maybe I stay here though. We vill see."

"I think she is schizophrenic," Mara said as she sliced apples, "She was taking some pills. I saw her sometimes."

Jona was clutching his thumb. "There is something not right about her. My thumb that she cut last month when we skinned the yearling hasn't healed, and it started hurting when she came today. There is some bad juju in the valley."

Isabelle looked at his thumb wide-eyed. "I'm getting some sage and I'm gonna smudge the whole property." She scampered off to procure the tools for the large scale spiritual cleanse.

The cleanse didn't work. No matter how many times Isabelle ran circles around the farm with a smoldering bundle of sage, the bad juju didn't stop. And Hanna continued to make appearances for three days.

She unexpectedly arrived in the yurt the next day dressed normally, sat at the table, took up a pair of scissors, and began to trim weed. Jona hid, and I took her back to Divinity Wind.

"Just give it time, Hanna. You need to focus on yourself and stay healthy."

She toyed with her fingers and smiled. "Maybe I stay," was all she said.

She arrived again and found Jona in his tent without anyone

seeing her. She pleaded with him that she was better. She apologized. She said she would behave. Jona pulled his composure together and took her back to the realm of Raj Ras.

"I was really clear this time. I apologized for potentially leading her on. I thanked her for all her help. And I told her that it was just better for everyone, and especially her, if she leaves. She said that she has friends in LA. I told her I would get her a bus ticket from Arcata, and she agreed it was best. But she denies that there is anything going on in her head... I didn't push the topic."

A week later, Jona was back from Arcata. We sat together in the cabin sharpening knives under the newly completed roof.

"Benji, she has an evil spirit in her. She seemed ok on the drive to Arcata. We even had some good laughs. I dropped her off at the bus station and gave her money for the ticket. A few hours later, I was in a shoe store getting Ezra new boots, and I looked out the window. Guess who was there watching us through the window?"

"What did you tell her?"

"Nothing, I got up to go out, and then she was gone. But... the next day I was in the park and Ezra and I were climbing a tree. I looked down, and fucking Hanna was standing at the base of the tree watching us. I kind of freaked out. I drove her to the bus station, bought the ticket myself and waited with her until the bus came."

I shook my head. "Wow. Well, you know what's crazy? The rain stopped when you guys left. That's why I managed to finish the roof."

He looked at me with nervous wonder. "That's pretty weird, because it started to rain in Arcata just as we got there, and it had been clear all week. It poured on Halloween. And my thumb stopped hurting when the bus left. Well, I feel much better now. She is in LA. The story of Hanna is over."

6

The reprieve from the rain did not last long—it returned with renewed force to castigate us, seemingly for the mere audacity of trying to survive. My days were spent in vigilance, attending to the needs of the farm.

We moved a large part of the harvest from the dry rooms into the yurt, turning it into a forest of pungent garlands. The yurt was least vulnerable to weather, and had the woodstove, a source of heat not requiring the rather fickle commodity of electricity. Even the yurt was no fortress however, and I finally had to cut a hole in the tarp floor and dig a pit for a sump pump because the French drains we'd dug as a moat surrounding the structure were immediately clogged with sediment, and the water so abundant, that they were no real prevention at all. The workers would remove their boots on an elevated pallet, and then leap across the pool that swelled just inside the front door. The pump was just powerful enough to keep the water level from increasing, and sometimes not even that, because the power regularly failed. I stocked the woodstove and lit candles, and then would dash through the darkness to the generator to kick it and scream at it and finally plead with it until it grumbled back to life.

The power outages were a constant problem and a hindrance to all work needing to be done at night. The farm was overcrowded, and everyone spent their time in the yurt or huddled in the damp kitchen. We had two small generators, but those were necessary to run the fans and the dehumidifiers in the fragile dry rooms that were still packed with the recent harvest, so we relied on the larger engine to run the rest of the farm. Some nights, Hunter, Jona, and I had to fight the generator for hours. When we managed to get the power back, we would return to the yurt to discover everyone else had abandoned it, gone to their respective tents to hide from the misery outside. We would groan that our work had been for naught, and then realize that for a brief moment we could relax and enjoy the crackling woodstove in silence. It was a strange sensation to live on forty acres, yet feel crowded and confined to just a few dry spaces.

I spent as much time working on the cabin as I could. Nobody went there. Jona was somewhat removed, lost in his own head and busy with Ezra, so I worked alone until I was needed in the yurt. I recalled the feelings of my first experience in the yurt at Constance and Derek's farm, industrial and familial all at once. It was the same here—we worked hard, but we worked hard together. And in the evenings, we ate together with smiles and laughter, and forgot the travails of the world because our problems, in the end, were minor. We lived in a fairytale where the floods and the fights and the frustrations were only epic in their intent to create a story of that time, and in that way the trials became laughable, and even loved.

"When you are making history, the mundane suddenly becomes much more important and exciting, because it's the mundane that weaves the story together. It's the mundane that becomes the lessons." The light from the woodstove made Hunter's already orange hair look like a wreath of flame around his face.

"When you are changing the world, the way you do each small thing is representative, or symbolic, of your greater trajectory. That's why I don't mind these little hardships like no electricity. It's all just symbolic of the brave pilgrim, willing to suffer in order to make change."

The silent group nodded solemnly to the fire, and the rain paused so that the valley itself could lean in closer to hear of its role in the shaping of human affairs.

"When we lose power at home, we are helpless. We have to wait for the city to fix it, which is annoying and inconvenient. Here, whether we fix it or not, it is a triumph. If we fix it, we have taken care of ourselves. If we don't, we realize we don't actually need it."

The group of strangers from around the world were hunkered in the mud. To the outside observer it might have appeared as though humanity was regressing, but they all smiled because they knew they were part of a great step forward.

"Each of us is so much more than ourselves here. Each is a character in this story and each moment we pass here is an important note in the crafting of a canon. Some people imagine a philosophy and shape it with their thoughts; some people live a philosophy and shape it with their actions."

The darkness absorbed Hunter's words and recorded them in its eternity. The sounds of rain on the kitchen roof returned so that the silence could retreat to cogitate on histories and futures, thoughts and actions.

7

Nicolas Husk arrived with his son, Alden, and Ezra had his best friend again. They immediately ran off into the rain to find dead animals to play with.

Nick was as large as a mountain, and had a ruddy glow, like a volcano. He smiled when others were happy and liked a good party. His presence was naturally large, so he embraced it, and used it to express abundance in all manners.

He burst through the door with two bottles of tequila in his hammy fists, and a joint the size of a bowling pin between his lips. His long, blond hair was plastered to his head.

"WOW! We are having a party here. Look at all of these BEAUTIFUL PEOPLE!"

It could be said a second time that he loved a party... and parties loved him. And when he saw the yurt packed wall to wall with people, he saw it as a celebration. He seemed to fill the front half of the yurt as his excitement grew.

"Look who I ran into on the way in!"

The statement was more of a way to create some extra excitement in the room than to share news and he failed to reveal *who* it was hidden behind him. Nick was busy acquiring the energy from the interior and absorbing it all so that it would be part of him, increasing his greatness like a balloon so he could explode outwards like a joyous Big Bang and return the energy ten-fold.

Trailing him was a lank, fidgeting figure.

"Brooke!"

I tiptoed around the puddle that had usurped the place of a doormat and gave Brooke a hug. More figures were trying to crowd in—Tempo and Lena and Brooke's girlfriend, Kathleen, squashed in behind Nicolas, who was filling the room with his laughter and occupying ever more of the yurt with his monumental form. Even Tempo looked small near him.

Two more friends from the Oregon enclave arrived with them as well—supposedly, they were the last trimmers. The Oregonians ran to greet them. The excitement was growing and the frenzy of energy was growing with it. Nicolas Husk finally bellowed with laughter and flung himself on the room, dragging all twenty inhabitants into an embrace so emphatically loving that every person managed to be in contact with every other person. He finally dropped his arms with a sigh of pleasure and pulled the lid from the tequila bottle.

We were just settling into a cozy and intimate evening of close proximity and reacquainting with old friends when the door opened and three more figures entered—grave, and overwhelmed by the crowd. Ines and Julia cried with joy and went to the door to embrace their friends. Jona rose and greeted the newcomers as well.

As it turned out, he had agreed to the presence of these two additional trimmers at the request of Ines. They were Argentines, and one of the girls had brought her partner without invitation, but with the hope that he could help with the farm work. I looked at the yurt and the dizzying number of bodies. It was already midway through the season, and we certainly didn't need any more help—with the farm or with the trimming. Jona welcomed them nevertheless, and they joined the throng. Jona stood by the door looking bewildered and then slipped out into the rain.

Nick roamed the yurt giving each trimmer crushing massages and engulfing them in loving hugs of exuberance. He poured tequila into any unguarded and open mouth and burned through joints as fast as they were rolled. English language washed around the room until Spanish reformed and overtook it, and then the English escalated in volume, and the Spanish built upon itself to keep a footing, and the general volume increased. The yurt thrummed with noise.

Brooke sat for a time looking forlorn.

"How you doing, man?"

He studied me for a moment, looking at the connection with another soul. The darting in his eyes was stronger than ever. "Oh, things are pretty good. We are busy at Kathleen's place." He half glanced at the chaos of the room. "Things are pretty different here it seems."

I exhaled. "This place changes fast. It's a different world here, Brooke."

He nodded. "Lots of people," he remarked.

"Yeah, well, more this minute than ever before. And you know the rain. It's not very fun to roam around outside."

We discussed the quality of the plants that season, and technical aspects of farm life. Finally, he stood and wandered out of the yurt, not a smile on his face.

"He has been pretty down all season," Tempo said.

"His girlfriend wants a baby!" Lena confided with a loud whisper. *"He isn't ready, but she is putting the pressure on. Her clock is saying, Baby! Now!"* Lena laughed, cool and calm. "He'll be all right. There is always stress during the season, but our place is relaxed, pretty quiet. Not like this."

Tempo glanced at Kathleen across the room. "Brooke doesn't have any backbone about it. He doesn't tell her that he wants to wait. He just mopes. It's kind of annoying. But whatever, it's his deal."

Lena offered me a mushroom. "Just to add a little sparkle to the room?"

I winked at her. "Why not?"

I was enjoying lively banter with Nick and my old friends when the door creaked open and Jona slunk into the room holding a shawl across his face, silent in movement, screaming with intention. The room instinctually fell quiet.

He stammered. His masculine, powerful frame looked small and fragile. "I, I have made a mistake." He kept the shawl across his face in shame. The room resonated with waiting stillness. "I felt so much energy, so I took a bath and I smoked opium, and I considered the farm, and the community, and I realized that we have too many people for the sustainability of the land and for the health of everyone here." He revealed his face and his eyes were filled with weariness. He looked at the three Argentines who were still joyously reuniting with their friends. "I need to ask you to leave. We don't have a space for you here."

There was a moment of startled digestion, and then the Argentine man sprang up in anger, pointing a finger at Jona. He yelled in Spanish and his partner rose to hold him. I watched the rift grow across the room like the earth opening. The factions were immediate and clear. Jona fled. The entire Latino population stood, silently donned their shoes, and swept from the room. The angry Argentine was the last. He stared with rage at the door where Jona had left.

Nick looked around, drunk and happy. He saw the solemn faces. "Oh, so does this mean the party is over?" He was crestfallen.

8

The Latinos, in solidarity, threatened to leave. I avoided the lengthy processing that took place in the yurt the next day. Jona declared a day of rest for the farm, and nobody knew where to spend time since the yurt had become a conference center and the kitchen was damp and drafty. In the end, most went to Lassy for a day in the *city*.

I spent the morning with Brooke, and Lena, and Tempo, before they headed back over the hills to their farm. The weather wasn't at its worst, so when they departed, I headed up onto the roof of the cabin to work on the gutters.

Jona and Nick notified me that they would be immersed in negotiations and I waved them off hoping they would leave me to work. I was pleased to have a day free of distraction. From my vantage, I could see the door of the yurt, closed with purpose. I guessed it would remain closed for some time; the tension was high. I looked up the driveway and stretched my hands upwards and took a deep breath of personal contentment... then paused. There was a blonde head bobbing down the driveway. My throat went dry. It was a form I could identify from a mile away.

I dismounted the roof and sprinted through the mud up the driveway, slipping and sliding the whole way, running recklessly, knowing it was not possible to fall because I was driven by necessity. I intercepted the arrival halfway up the drive.

"Hello, Hanna."

Hanna beamed at me. "Hi, Benji, I decide to come back!"

I allowed myself to laugh. "Oh, Hanna, you are an impressive being, you know?"

Her smile expanded and her eyes twinkled. "Ya, I know."

I looked down at the thin snake of smoke sliding from the chimney in the yurt. "Let's take a walk, Hanna, you know I can't let you onto the land, right?"

"I know."

She shrugged and we headed up the driveway from where she had come. "I sink maybe I just come and stay for a while. I vill be good, I promise."

I shook my head. "Hanna, this is a complicated situation, and unfortunately you chose a really bad time to come back. Jona has a lot to deal with right now. His job has a lot of responsibility, more than we understand. There are more than twenty people living here and we barely have the ability to take care of them. We don't have power half the time, everyone is tired and uncomfortable, and everyone has their own personal problems. You aren't the only drama in Tipsytom. Jona feels the weight of all of that. The farm needs stability right now, as much as it can get. I want to try to explain this to you so that you understand, ok?"

She nodded. "Yes, I always like talking with you, Benji. You always listen."

I threw an arm over her shoulder. "We are both going to try to understand, Hanna. Let me offer an opinion. I think you were hurt by your relationship with Jona, which is natural, and maybe he didn't deal with it in the best way, but at this time and in this place, he is focused on something greater than the individual. You got the bad end of that deal, I know. He can't spend his energy on one relationship though, because in his position, the community is the most important entity. The more attention you needed as an individual, the greater his stress became. This is a place of business remember, whether we like it or not. The business has to function for the community to exist, and that requires that the individuals be strong. They are the working parts of the machine. They need enough individual attention and care for the whole to work, but it is the functionality of the greater machine that wins in the end. And if a part is broken, it has to be discarded. It sounds harsh, but our farm is still new and fragile and it can't risk failure."

Hanna listened intently and then sighed a very long exhale. "Maybe I just say sorry. I'm better now. I promise."

We were almost at the front gate. "Hanna, it really isn't a good time. The best way for you to do the right thing is to not be here right now. In time, yes, you can communicate with Jona. And I am sure, when things have calmed down, he will be more receptive, but right now... no. There are too many other problems. By the way, how the hell did you get here? We all thought you were in LA."

A sly look passed across her face. "I have my ways!"

"Well, clever girl, you are going to tell me those *ways* because you aren't staying here, and I need to figure out how to ship you out of the valley. So?"

She pouted a moment. "Ok, I get off the bus in Santa Barbara, and I meet some guy, and he fall in love with me, and I made him bring me here." Her proud smile returned.

I whistled. "You are really something. So you managed to

convince a guy to drive you all the way out here? That's at least five hundred miles, Hanna."

She wriggled with delight. "And he was going south when he picks me up, so he turned around for me. He really love me!"

"You are crazy."

Her strange smile never faded. "Yes, I know."

The guy was still there, parked in a pull-off near the tavern, just another naïve young man ensnared by the guiles of love.

"Hey, man, sorry you drove all the way out here, but Hanna isn't allowed on the property at the moment." I explained a censored version of the situation to him.

His response contained no surprise, "Yeah, I figured something was up. She couldn't ever really give me a straight answer about why she left. It's cool. I didn't really have anything going on."

Hanna giggled and looked coy. "He is a nice guy."

He was. I liked his style, and I feared for his heart.

"Well, is there any way you can take her away?"

We both looked at Hanna who was doing her best to look sweet.

"Yeah, man, no problem. Want to head south again, Hanna?"

The sun suddenly found a rift in the clouds.

"Be careful with this one. C'mere and give me a hug, Hanna. You will be all right. Just take care of that head."

When I got back to the land many of the farm's inhabitants had gathered in the sunlight outside of the yurt. The smiles had returned. Words had been said, feelings expressed, and calls made. Linda and her husband needed trimmers on the other side of the valley, and the Argentines would go there. Raj Ras had a room for rent.

"They just have to figure out how to get around since they can't stay where they are working," Ines said.

"Take my car. I don't need it. They can have it for the rest of the season." They looked at me with surprise. "It's all good, you guys need it. And Aaron keeps stealing it anyway, so it's already at Divinity Wind half the time."

The angry Argentine man abruptly walked up and embraced me.

It was strange to see Helga driving around the valley the rest of the season. She was probably less neglected than she had been for a long time.

"Fuck, man, things have been crazy this season," Jona opined.

I nodded. We were up on the roof working in the sunshine. "I mean, I can't imagine how things could have gotten any crazier." I drove another nail. I decided not to tell him about the visitor.

"Yeah, me neither."

9

It was suddenly late in the season. The leaves had been well stomped into the earth, and weariness was in the air. It was a time when people wondered if they could live in this manner indefinitely, considered the fact that communal existence was not the standard living formula, and mused on why humans hadn't reverted to subsistence living—or something close to it.

When I was discouraged and exhausted, I would remind myself that this was the peak of the intensity and work, and it was the foreshadowing of winter whispering about a calm time ahead, luring the mind towards hibernation. It was simply the time in the cycle when weariness could be expected.

Tiffany, Isabelle, Raj Ras, and I were lying on the floor of his sanctuary. We were coming out of the arcane dimensions of ayahuasca, and the ceiling was swimming softly, the scent of spruce incense still conjuring images of silent forests in the rapture of untouched snow.

"Raj... do you think we are at the end of an era, like we are trying to salvage what we can before everything collapses? Or the beginning of one, like the start of something new and great?"

Raj allowed the silence to explore itself and become comfortable again before he replied to Tiffany's inquiry, letting his soft and slightly lumpy voice compliment the silence with a touch of sound. "Those two scenarios don't have to be separate. It is a matter of scale. If you are asking about a cosmic shift in the universe, I really don't know. I ask the ayahuasca spirit this question all the time, but it remains silent on that subject. If it is an ending or a beginning, maybe only the keenly aware here on our plane of existence will perceive it. If you are talking about eras on our planet, well, for some there are endings, and for some beginnings, and some are right in the middle of something. Life has landmarks for us at different times. You, for example, have just come to California and feel the excitement to grow here and join something that is new and different. You see potential and a future. I'm old. I've been in the valley eight years. I'm not a farmer. I'm lonely. Everyone in town is afraid of me. I live in a dumpy old hotel...

"No!" he stopped Tiff from protesting this.

"It's true. All I want to do is sell the place and stop making incense. What am I doing here? Nobody comes here to learn from me anymore. My era is done. So you see, ends and beginnings are around us everywhere, and we need to understand the monumental shifts in our own lives... But I know, you are thinking of all of the farmers coming to the valley. Are they escapees trying to find a moment of peace during the great decline? Or, are they pioneers arriving to build the new era?"

Tiffany nodded her head as she stared up at the ceiling. Raj didn't see, but he understood.

"Yes, both, it is a start, and an end, and a moment in the middle. As things are right now… well, they won't stay, they will change. They have been changing constantly. If this event in time is spreading ideas that are going to lead to new experiments with living, then yes. Will it change society in a fundamental way? I don't know. Maybe it is just one step in that process."

Raj Ras stopped and listened to the silence for a time.

"But a step is important. Each step is important to reach a goal. It could also be a step towards the end of a paradigm too, however."

Raj Ras sat up, smiling like a child. "Mmm, very good question, Tiff! That one made us think, didn't it?"

In my mind, Raj Ras went from the role of shaman to kindergarten teacher in an instant, and I began to laugh.

Isabelle snorted next to me and began to laugh too. "You are such a dork, Raj!" she squealed. "I would come learn from you!"

He smiled with startled pleasure as though nobody had said this in quite some time.

"Oh good, Izzy. Well, we can learn things together, because a good teacher is a good student. That is what the ayahuasca spirit always tells me. I'll say this—if you want to be part of an era that is beginning, well, don't be the end. Be the beginning."

10

The men on the farm preferred to slop through the mud on some invented errand, or shiver in the kitchen rather than occupy the yurt. There were fourteen women and one man holed up in the confining cylinder.

"It's not that bad!" Pelli defended and smacked my arm. "But our cycles are all aligned now so we are all on our periods, and you know, things can get emotional."

I nodded. "And you have all been sitting in a room together for a month-and-a-half. I knew there would be blood one way or another." I grinned roguishly and Pelli scowled.

"Well, that's what you do when you trim. And you endure it because you make great fucking money and you don't have to work half the year."

The door to the yurt banged open and we could hear the sound of crying.

"Oh God!" Pelli rolled her eyes. "The red tent! The Latina girls always speak in Spanish and I think they are talking shit about us. And Sandra has been on her period for like, three weeks, and she is an emotional disaster and keeps trying to get us all to go out and bleed on the ground together, and Julia whistles unconsciously and its really obnoxious, and I love her to death, but Kayla is a chronic cherry-picker, and I don't think I can listen to another Radio Lab podcast."

I reached over and gave Pelli a big hug. "Yep, you have been stuck in a room with the same people for too long. We are gonna be out of here soon, don't worry."

"Haha, yeah, I'm bitching about it, but as soon as I leave, I will miss it all. It always feels weird going back to my normal life. It kind of feels like going backwards, ya know? It's like exercising everyday and getting fit, and feeling good, and then stopping it all and getting fat. Hahaha."

"That's a curious way of putting it," I said, "but I get you. It's challenging to be here, but you are doing something really good for yourself, and growing. And then going home feels like letting go of all the progress you made. But you don't have to let go of that stuff, you know."

"I know," Pelli said with a sigh. "I try to take it back to my other existence, but it is kind of hard when the people around you aren't trying to grow or change. Here everyone wants to do the work to make their lives better. It's easier when you are around motivated people, and harder when you are around people who don't care at all, or don't know how."

"I don't know, Pelli," I replied. "Maybe you are taking back more than you realize."

I went back to one of the hoop houses where Nick and I were making bubble hash. The long half-cylinder structure was covered with a translucent tarp, making it glow during daylight hours. The weed that had been drying there was all gone, systematically emptied out and trimmed.

We were well bundled in layers of clothing, but still our teeth chattered. The temperature was marginally above freezing, and the process of making bubble hash required the regular submergence of hands into trashcans of ice water.

Nick and I had collected all the trim from the processed buds, which we collected at the end of each day from the trimmers. Now it was piled around us in capacious garbage bags, ready to be processed into hash.

"This is gonna make a lot of hash, I imagine."

Nick chuckled with his whole great body. "No way, Benji, we are going to get a ball of hash about the size of a grapefruit out of all this. Everything from the garden—one wonderful grapefruit. I like to use if for gifts, or for my head stash. Hard to find a market for it. It's not enough, and the laws on hash production are pretty harsh.

Not protected like the medical buds are."

We upended one of the plastic bags into a trashcan and pressed it under the ice. Needles of pain shot through my hands as they were swallowed by frigid water.

"We're gonna mix it all together, except the Blue Dream and the Head Band. I want to try those pure. Hand me that mixer."

I passed him the hand-held cement mixer, a sinister device that looked like a three-foot long electric eggbeater. Nick Husk brandished it like a toy sword and then crammed it into the water. There was a belch and a spray and then the water leapt into a verdant life form.

"Hehehe, I love how fast the water turns that lime-green color. Some people drink it, but I prefer to just smoke the stuff. Maybe we can make chai with the liquid."

We took turns running the mixer and sucking our fingers for warmth.

"The THC crystals become brittle in the cold water and when you agitate them with the mixer, they break away from the plant matter. Then we just have to strain out the plant residue."

We systematically poured the soup through increasingly fine sieves until on the seventh filter, the sandy remains were of a light enough hue that Nick was satisfied.

"Cool, we should be able to do another round with that same batch and get some more." He squeezed the water from the sieve and let it run across his hand.

"I kind of like being cold." He took off his jacket and lit a joint.

When Nick was not at play, he was at work, and his countenance changed. He would puff through joints in silence and deftly handle his tasks, forcing them to go the way he wanted. His face became stone and often he wouldn't perceive others—they were just parts of a process. But just as the switch flipped and he became a steel machine, the switch would flip the other way and he would suddenly turn on his smile and glow red, his voice like an earthquake.

Jona brought a thermos of warm tea, a welcome gift. We huddled around the hash cans pretending they contained fire while Jona inspected the results.

"Crazy that this can get you into so much trouble."

Nick heaved another trash can full of ice, water, and plant matter into the bin with the sieves. His arms, now bare, bulged. He talked through clenched lips that fiercely gripped the joint. "It's all medicine. This is just the stronger dose!" he shook with laughter and beamed at us, once again, become his jovial half, then tossed the empty can aside and sucked passionately at the glowing stick in his mouth.

"It's medicine. I have seen it change lives. People with physical suffering, and heart suffering, or emotional or psychological! Whatever it is, this stuff can help. It's a gift from Gaia."

Jona stared at the sodden plant matter. "Yes, it is medicine. It is powerful and can be abused, but I think the vast majority of its use helps people. I am hearing about new studies all the time, looking at how it is relief for cancer patients, and people in serious pain."

Nick was stirred by these words and interjected, "I feel like a freedom fighter! I love it. I always think I have the best job, ya know? Growing medicine that will help a bunch of folks! Gotta get the medicine to the people! We are fighting the good fight!" He stomped around and threw his hands into the air in exaltation. "Bring the medicine to the people! Bring them laughter and smiles!"

Jona refilled my cup with tea.

"So, Benji, this seems like a good time to bring up an idea Nick and I had. We need to make some smart money decisions because the price of a pound in Northern California has dropped a lot in the last couple of years. The market is flooded, especially after the season."

Nick chimed in again. "Yeah, like two years ago, it was pretty easy to sell a pound for three thousand bucks, or right at the end of the season maybe twenty-eight hundred. And you could go down to LA and get five grand! Those were good times!"

Jona continued. "Now all the offers I'm getting are like, eighteen hundred at best. And we will probably have to sell some for twelve here soon, just to be able to pay the trimmers. So it's making us think about other options. Nick has a friend with a connection on the East Coast. New York City, I think. We should be able to sell pounds for forty-two to forty-five there. But we need someone to get it over there."

They both watched me, the question already presented without the need for words.

"Go on," I said.

"Well, you are pretty much the only person we trust to do it right now, so we wanted to make you the offer. I'm not sure if we will go for it if you say no. It is definitely risky, so it's completely up to you and we'll understand if you don't want to, but if anyone can do it, it's you." Jona forced a chuckle, and the tension that had crowded in around us dissipated somewhat.

I felt strange. I immediately thought of the repercussions. We all stared into the green potion slowly spinning in the trash barrel. *Medicine for the people.*

11

The evening we finished trimming we had a bonfire and burned the skeletal remains of the plants. We danced naked around the monument to our accomplishments and then dove into the frosty water of the creek. I stayed by the fire until it was a flat bed of glowing embers, the remnants of many months sweat and energy. Another ending and another beginning.

I retrieved my car the following day from the Argentines who were finishing the work for Linda. Everyone was quite pleased by how things had transpired. They spoke of fate and serendipity. To me it seemed like the chaos of chance with a bit of human desire to help others on a day-to-day basis.

Linda said that she was burnt-out running the bar and that they were thinking of selling it.

"Maybe Henry will buy it back!"

She rolled her eyes. "He can't afford it. Someone will want it. It's the only entertainment in the whole valley."

"The valley itself is entertainment. I have never been bored here."

She laughed a warm and genuine laugh. "No, one doesn't get bored here."

Cormac, Jona, and I were the last to leave the farm. Cormac was walking without his crutches, and was even capable of minor physical tasks. Jona and I hung the last windows in the cabin. The simple pole frame cabin we built the previous year for our survival had transformed into a house during the last few months. We closed the newly hung door on our way out.

"I can almost call it a home!" Jona said, observing it from the top of the driveway. He shook his head. "Things change so fast here."

Midway to the coast, Jona spotted a dead deer on the road. He turned on his hazards and pulled over. Cormac and I pulled up behind him. The deer was big and fresh. We wrapped a tarp around it and deposited the carcass in the back of the truck.

"Nick sent me a text and said the party at his house on the coast is underway. Let's bring them fresh meat!"

Nick's house on the coast was popularly known as The Rock Star House. He was renting it while his wife, Carmen, was pregnant. She wasn't interested in living on a haphazard farm with no amenities, far from civilization during her pregnancy, so they found a coastal palace instead, built on cliffs above the sea where the spray of the rambunctious waves reached eagerly for the floorboards of the deck.

"We work hard in the mud half the year," Nick explained. "Might as well live in style the other half. I work so my family can have a comfortable life!"

Carmen had announced that everyone on the farm was invited to The Rock Star House for a post-season party, and the event was well underway when we pulled up and dragged the dead deer into the backyard.

While Jona and I organized a place to skin and butcher the carcass, Cormac went on a reconnaissance mission to determine the mood of the party. He returned five minutes later.

"They are all high on LSD... like, super high... And I just dosed too." He grinned broadly. "I ain't skinning no deer tonight!" He cackled and darted away into the shadows.

I settled next to the deer, inserted my skinning knife beneath its dermis, and began to work the blade up the belly. Commotion erupted from the back door of the house. It was Nick and ten ladies. Nick thundered across the yard like a baby giant, blubbering and babbling, and then collapsed on the deer.

"OHH, beloved life form! Precious soul!" he cried into its nape. "We give thanks for your life! Your sacred life!" He hugged the deer to him, rocking back and forth.

I slowly withdrew my knife.

The girls were gaping.

Tiffany brightened with an idea. "We need to hold space guys! Let's sit in circle and feel gratitude for this beautiful life."

The others simply looked amazed and then plopped down on the grass, forming a distorted circle around us. Nick continued to clench the deer and weep. The deer, for its part, was less than expressive. Jona had become silent and sensitive, and I could see he was intently focused on his task. Julia began to *Om*, and the others joined in. Nick produced a blade, and impaled the flank of the dead beast, unable to find the proper location for his knife through his day-glo tears.

Mara rose ominously from the shadows, a look of distant fixation in her eyes. "I must be part of this process. It is the cycle of life." A knife keened as it emerged from her garments, and she descended on the prey.

Tiffany looked on, and suddenly maddened by jealousy, retrieved one of Jona's blades and joined the fray. Ines pulled a knife from her boot. The group had undertaken a difficult and somewhat strangled chant.

They all carry blades, I thought. I shied.

Jona was calmly attempting to manage the butchery, speaking softly, indicating the proper places to cut, the tension in his voice only vaguely disguised.

"I'm out!" I said, "Too many people."

They hardly noticed.

There were many unfamiliar faces at the party. Our group comprised about half of them. Carmen reigned in the living room with several soon-to-be mothers. I introduced myself.

"Oh, Benji! It's great to meet you. Would you like some acid or

MDMA?" The pregnant gals can't participate, so we are all here to make sure everyone stays safe tonight."

Cormac was in the corner making out with a shadowy woman, and Aaron was on the deck howling at the ocean and screaming epithets at Poseidon. Pelli was floundering in a beanbag chair and gasping for help through hiccoughs and giggles. Virginia was cheerleading for Pelli, championing her escape, but finding it absolutely impossible to help, fearful of falling prey to the beanbag herself. Hunter stood blinking at the foot of the stairs, very, very lost.

"Um, I had better have a bit of both."

Carmen smiled. "Ok, that sounds like a good idea. You guys have been working hard. Now it's time to play."

Aaron pranced up to me like a goat and forcefully grabbed my face. He licked my cheek without reservation and attempted to impart his feelings with trembling eyeballs.

"You are so *weird!*" he growled, "I will always love you. *Forever!*"

He ran with gangly and comic intention onto the deck and flung himself into the hot tub fully clothed where Jona, through some miraculous shift of time and space, was wrapped up with a sometimes lover he had invited for the event, no longer concerned with the fate of the deer. Aaron flopped in the water like a fish until Nick finally dragged him out and tossed him like a discarded bone. Aaron dragged himself dramatically to the edge of the deck and looked at the sea again. He tilted his head back and screamed at the sky, "FOREVVVEEERRRR!"

I went in search of Isabelle and sat with her for a time in an upstairs room with carpet and curtains and the quaint commodities of a home, watching the darkened sea make war on the cliffs. A distance had formed between us and she wanted to be alone.

"Everything ends," she said miserably and then smiled.
I didn't smile.

The familiar feeling of emptiness rose inside me. All the energy seemed futile—making friends and becoming an integral part of these people's lives, the daily living newness, and exploring the unknown with them. But starting the next day, I would never see most of them again.

I walked outside and sat down with Hunter near the cliff to share my thoughts, which were beginning to bend and blossom in my mind like the sea below me. He listened and smiled.

"The impact we have on one another is eternal, Ben. If none of us sees one another again on this plane of existence, the experience still remains. It is indelible. Goodbyes can feel like a loss, but these experiences of life are building cumulatively to tell a story of people in a time and place, and that story will travel and be shared with others. We are part of a history that is much bigger and more important than our individual relationships. And that is comforting."

Hunter ran a hand through his orange beard. "I gotta stop pulling on my beard." He looked over and caught me doing the same. "You have to also. It will make us crazy. Want to go shave our beards off? Holy *shit*, I'm tripping really hard."

I assented. The deer was getting a haircut. It seemed like a good night for it.

The deer was eventually dismantled and the cycle of life somewhat furthered. There was a glow in the east where new days came from, and the community, with whom I had lived the last few months, was spread out on the cliffs. We had disbanded already, lost in our own reveries and starting down divergent paths.

Book Three

Part 3

1

I made it back to the Rock Star House one blustery afternoon in early winter. I talked with Carmen for a moment in the living room where little Alden pounced on me, desperate for a playmate. It was clear that my thoughts were elsewhere, so Carmen sent me to the garage with a meek smile to see Jonah and Nick.

I was distressed to find they were still packaging the ganja.

"Looks like I'm not gonna hit the road with daylight, huh?"

Nick scowled. I could feel the anxiety reverberating around the room. "The other guy, Ronnie, isn't even here yet. I sent him a text and he says he is still an hour away. So, we just get to wait and relax!" He looked at me and a smile split his huge blond face. "Benji! How about hugs! We haven't even said hi!"

I waded through the piles of vacuum-sealed bags and greeted them.

"Hey, Benji," said Jonah, choosing his sensitive voice.

I helped them finish packing and vacuum sealing the pounds. I wished I hadn't. I took one look at the pile and imagined one of the seals being a dud and the incriminating smell filling the trunk and making stealthy progress into the cab unbeknownst to my acclimated nose. I put that thought out of my mind and tried to convince myself that we knew what we were doing.

I had seen the boys in various modes of serious, but never so grave as that day. We sat in the living room and Nick rolled a column of herb into a paper.

"Gotta give thanks for the medicine," he remarked with a dry laugh and offered it my way.

"No thanks," I said.

Jonah suddenly spoke. "Benji, I got a call from Brooke just a couple of hours ago. I know this might sound pretty crazy, but he got busted this morning in Kansas."

I didn't respond, but all my internal organs suddenly felt foreign.

"He and his girlfriend were heading to Atlanta on I-70 with twenty pounds. I guess there was a sign on the freeway that said they were doing routine drug searches ahead and they freaked out and took the first exit... well, the exit was where the search was. Those fuckers are clever. They know a nervous driver is going to try to dodge the trap and take the exit."

Nick stared at the burning end of his joint and growled, "Those sneaky fuckers."

I couldn't handle any more suspense. "Well, what the fuck happened to him? Is he in jail?"

Jonah smiled, but it wasn't a happy smile. "That's the craziest part. Brooke said that the cops just robbed him. He and Kathleen pulled up at the stop and the cops made them get out of the car. They had a dog there that gave them some sort of sign that it smelled something. I doubt it actually smelled a thing, but when it indicates there is something there, the cops have a right to search, so they got into the car and found all the bud. Then, Brooke said, the cops took their names and a little bit of info and told them to just get the hell out of there—didn't book them or anything."

Nick shook his head in disbelief. "Brooke is fuckin lucky, he could have been calling and looking for bail."

I couldn't believe it. "They just let him go?" I repeated stupidly.

Jonah nodded. "Kept his fuckin weed and let him go. The cops want their cut too."

We all contemplated this for a few moments, then Jonah resumed. "I had to let you know that before you go. You know we will understand if you don't feel good about it, or if you want another day to think."

I took some time and watched the stormy sea, which already seemed like a stranger. For some reason I was more upset about leaving the sea behind than anything else. I knew transporting the weed was basically just a flat-out stupid idea, but I had spent so much time thinking about the trip and pepping myself up that I couldn't imagine withdrawing. There was the money, of course, but for me, there was that old thirst for adventure in need of slaking, and I was feeling that absurd stirring of confidence and invincibility that made my logical side groan every time it surfaced. Despite any new development, I knew I was going.

Ronnie showed up with the rain, and it started to feel real… or maybe surreal. I couldn't tell if I was hyperaware of every word and action, making them all seem very important and memorable, or if I was in a movie where all the lines and choreography were set. They handed me a track phone with two numbers in it. Nick was going under the code name *Tennessee*, and my connection, who would call me when I neared the East Coast, was apparently *Raptor*. I couldn't think of a cool name for myself, but I would have a long drive to invent any number of pseudonyms.

Ronnie was an agitated individual and regarded me with mistrust. I responded in kind. I didn't like that this other guy was involved, but it was his friend who had the connection in New York, so it was unavoidable.

"Can we trust this guy?" Ronnie asked Nick right in front of me. "I mean, no offense, but I have a lot riding on this."

I held my tongue.

Nick looked annoyed but replied in his tone of eternal cool. "Yeah, we wouldn't have asked him if we couldn't trust him."

We talked business, but there wasn't really much to say. I would drive east and Raptor would call me in four days and give me instructions. We had rented a car and it was waiting at the Portland airport. If things really went to hell, they would pay my legal fees, but we didn't want to talk about that. It all sounded so professional by tone, but I could tell that the guys new as little about how this stuff worked as me. Ronnie seemed unsure about parting with his herb, and my guys were clearly anxious.

Finally, Nick said, "Just call me if you really need something."

I nodded. "All right. Sooner I get going the sooner the people get their medicine right?" I winked and there was a relieved chuckle. Even if I wasn't particularly relaxed, it wouldn't do anything to let the guys think I was anything but calm and confident.

Jonah confirmed it. "That's right, Benji. You know I wouldn't let you go if I didn't think you were the one who could handle it."

2

It was dark, and a storm well underway when I headed north in

Helga with forty pounds of vacuum-sealed marijuana packed tightly into three big dry bags. I glanced in the rear view mirror at the luggage. The bags took up the better part of my wagon's trunk space. *I can't wait to get this stuff into a locked trunk in Portland,* I thought.

The paranoia didn't hold off to give me time to acclimate. It was there the moment I climbed into my car. It settled into the seat next to me, comfortable, and prepared to be my companion for the duration of the long drive. The more I tried to relax and think of my trip north to Portland as just routine, the more uncomfortable I became. The roads were deserted, the people shut away in their houses, protected from the storm and the night. Each time I passed through a little town and waited at a stop light on the empty highway, I would glance around, nervous that the police were observing from a side alley, waiting for the evildoers who came out under the cover of foul weather and darkness. Every time I saw headlights, I was sure it was the police. Who else would be driving in these conditions? I began to obsess over the shapes of the headlights as they approached, trying to develop my recognition. If I saw a police vehicle approaching, I needed the maximum period of time to... I stopped myself. I just needed to drive. That was all.

I called my friend John Brewer and landed at his house in Portland. He was imperturbable.

"So you are making a drive. Hmm, that's cool." He popped the cap off a beer and stuck it in my hand as if he was putting something on the shelf where it always went. "You feel pretty good about it?"

I put down a large part of the beer and slumped into an easy chair. I wondered if this was how Frodo felt in Rivendale. Brewer's place would be the last friendly house before the wilds. "No, not really, but I'm in it, and I'm gonna do it."

Brewer stuck his fingers into his tawny beard and slowly, thoughtfully scratched. "Hm. That's a pretty long trip. How long you think it's gonna take? Four days at least, if the weather is all right."

I nodded, "At least. I don't want to drive at night. I just want to be another car on the road."

He kept nodding. Brewer's voice was low and quiet and had the hint of a drawl. It was calming. "You have chains? It's December, man. Your chances of hitting snow are pretty good, unless you head way south. But you wouldn't be up here if you were taking the south route."

I grimaced. "Nah, I'm not going that way. I'm heading to New York, and those routes are pretty well watched from the stories I'm hearing." I didn't tell Brooke's story. I didn't want to think about it.

"Well, we can get you to the airport to pick up the car in the morning, and then I'm gonna make you go to Wal-Mart and get chains."

I acquiesced.

3

The car was cherry red. Brewer walked around it and inspected it. "You want to trade it in for something more subtle?"

It glowed even under the pale lights of the garage. I asked if they had other colors and they said it would take several hours. The pressures of the enterprise told me that I did not have time to wait.

"Well, it has a GPS panel. That's good. And it's a Toyota Corolla. It doesn't get much more generic than that."

The dry bags bearing my precious cargo filled the trunk. I had my snowboard and some gear—my idea of an excuse to be driving across the country in the winter. Between Oregon and the Rockies: *I was going to visit a friend in Colorado.* After that? *I'd heard the skiing was nice in the Ohio River Valley? I wanted to slide down an icy street in Pennsylvania?* Once again, I did the easy thing. I stopped thinking about it and stuffed the board and boots in the back seat.

"Brewer, you have any music? Old CDs or something I can borrow?" We looked through his collection.

"You can take all of these, and I don't care if I get them back."

I flipped through the CD binder. "Britney Spears?" I smiled for the first time that day.

"We all go through our phases, man. Like I said, I don't need these back."

I patted him on the shoulder. "You're a saint, Brewer. This will really distract me from the driving."

4

I felt much better on the freeway in daylight. The Columbia Gorge was gray and windy, but as I had hoped, I was just another car, albeit a bright red one.

After the errands of the morning, it was early afternoon before I managed to get out of Portland. And by the time I climbed into the Blue Mountains outside of Pendleton, the light had dimmed and thick snowflakes were plopping on the windshield. By La Grande, it was dark and I was already breaking my rule about night driving, but I had hoped to make it to Boise that first day and so decided to push on. The snow advanced quickly out of La Grande and I spent the next four hours making the drive to Ontario—a drive that should have taken half that time. I checked into a hotel exhausted and discouraged. Another slow and stressful day, and I hadn't even made it out of Oregon.

5

The discussion of *freedom* and its various forms and meanings is an easy undertaking from the safe location of a word processor. One can vehemently opine on any and every element of the word, as I am doing in this piece. One can discuss the *freedom* to live by chosen values, and the *freedom* to decide a lifestyle. One can discuss the *freedom* associated with where we go and what we do, and the people we interact with. In the United States, we are fortunate to have a great deal of self-determination. All discussions regarding these choices pertain to the medical marijuana industry and the new culture that has developed along with it, but there is another region of freedom that is much more black and white, and participating in an illegal business is skating along that very fine line of liberty where a debate does not simply end in walking away feeling like you made your point, or feeling offended that the other is an idiot and doesn't get the idea. I speak of the freedom that is discussed when laws are broken, a very tangible loss of personal autonomy, which the offering of an opinion or argument will not change—a question of one's liberty, which they do not get to choose for themselves. Incarceration!

On the farm, when the sun was shining and we looked at the cradling hills of the Tipsytom Valley, the growing of cannabis never felt illegal, at least not on a daily basis. And it was well understood by those present that the likelihood of any real trouble was remote, something that happened only to the arrogant and the foolish who ignored the *rules*. If you just worked within a reasonable distance of the medical marijuana laws, it was unlikely that you'd be hassled. When you left the comfort of the Northern California wilderness, however, the idealistic little universe cracked open and the eggshell began to fall away, and the *opinion* of the outside world, set down as *law*, was waiting.

When you left the farm where you were growing legal medical marijuana and got in a car with forty pounds of weed... you were a narcotics smuggler. Often that reality didn't sink in until the egg cracked wide open.

It started with an orange.

6

I sat in the driver's seat staring at the steering wheel, mindlessly peeling an orange, wondering again, or rather as part of an incessant chain of wonderment, what the hell I was thinking. On this third day, not even out of my home state, I was giddy with the realization that I was actually seeing this enterprise through, but also angry with myself that I was actually seeing it through, and disdainful of all of those thoughts because the only thing required to see it through was to simply drive a car.

The clock told me it was just before eight in the morning— daylight. I was going to drive through all of that daylight and not a minute more. There was precious little of it in mid-December, but that was my logic: safer in the day. But first, I was going to eat the orange. I glanced over at the passenger seat. Paranoia was still there, leering. I sighed and turned on the car.

There was no build up, no chance to let my thoughts find their fear. I had stayed in the last generic hotel in Oregon, only half a mile from the Idaho border. I found one of John Brewers CDs, *Tubthumper*, by Chumbawumba. I set the cruise control exactly at the speed limit. I wiped the orange residue from my fingers onto a tissue. *I get knocked down, but I get up again. You're never gonna keep me down!* It was a familiar old tune. I drove across the Snake River and I looked in the rearview mirror. "Hope to see you soon, Oregon my beloved. Wish me luck."

The Idaho side of the river failed to impress me. There was the vapid *Welcome to Idaho* sign, and the fields of iced dirt spreading out beyond. I looked at the digital thermometer. It was thirty-two degrees Fahrenheit: freezing point. I had been so distracted that morning that I hadn't noticed how cold it was. I looked in the rearview mirror. There were blue and red lights flashing.

7

Only one thought crossed my mind as the officer of the law walked purposefully towards my car. *Well, Benjamin, you have forty pounds of marijuana in your car and you have just been pulled over. Decide right now if you are going to jail or if you will drive away from this. And if you decide to be free... don't fuck up!*

When the officer leaned in the passenger window and studied me, I felt no panic, no fear, no pressure, mostly just amusement. I didn't put the facts of the situation out of my mind, instead, I embraced them and found them so absurd that they were laughable. I hadn't been pulled over for anything in years, and now, for no apparent reason, on a day I happened to be smuggling narcotics... laughable.

I waited patiently for the cop to speak and I studied him as he did me. He so precisely fit the stereotype of a policeman that I found I was fighting back a smile. He was white, overweight, had a crew cut, and wore aviator glasses.

"License and registration," he said, as if it were a line from a movie where a cop is supposed to be the most cop-ish he can be.

I got into the glove box and pulled out the documents. "Will you tell me why you pulled me over, sir? I am pretty positive I wasn't speeding."

He glanced at me. "I'm going to check your papers and then I will tell you why I pulled you over."

I wasn't sure if he was supposed to do that, but I thought compliance was the best course.

He ran my info, and I thought of very little while he was away, just that this situation had seemed so impossible—it was like living out my imagination. It was an improbable, laughable scenario.

"Mr. Allen, I will just have you step out of the car for a moment, and then I will tell you why I pulled you over."

I looked at him with surprise and then slowly removed my seatbelt, stepped out into the bitter air and walked to the back of the car where the officer waited.

"I would like to ask for your compliance to search your person," he said. It wasn't really a question.

"You want to frisk me?"

His face was expressionless. "Yes, Mr. Allen."

I nodded, "Well, ok."

He asked me to place my hands on the trunk of the car and then patted my sides and up into my armpits, and then slid his hands down the inside of my legs. I looked down at my hands on the trunk of the car. *There are forty pounds of weed an inch beneath my hands right now.* He finished his routine and I stepped back to face him. He looked stern and impassive. The fields of iced dirt spread out behind him.

"Where are you headed today, Mr. Allen?"

"Salt Lake," I said. "A friend of mine lives there and we are going to do some snowboarding."

"And how long do you intend to stay there?"

"Well, I need to get home for Christmas." I felt like I was speaking with a robot. His expression didn't even twitch.

"Well, I pulled you over because when you crossed the bridge you were out of control and swerving. Can you tell me what was going on?"

This was obviously completely fabricated bullshit. For a moment, all I could do was slowly shake my head and look ponderous. "Uh, I really don't know what you saw. I was paying attention to the road and I had cruise control on, so... yeah, I am pretty sure I had control the whole time."

"Well, you don't appear to be intoxicated, that was my main concern, so I will let you off with a warning this time. Slow down and pay attention to your driving. There is ice on the road."

It seemed to be my dismissal, so I smiled. "Of course I will, sir. I'll take it easy." I tried to look casual as I turned to leave.

"Actually...," his voice was wooden and my skin began to crawl. I glanced back. He was still watching me. "Would you mind if I ask you a few more questions?"

I nodded, quite aware that saying *no* was not an option. "All right, go ahead." He shifted his feet and folded his hands as though he were about to give a well-rehearsed speech. *He is a fucking robot,* I thought. *Where is this going?*

"I'm working with a police unit called *Intercept* and our job is to apprehend people trafficking large sums of money, narcotics, and weapons across state lines."

Yep, that is where this is going. Un-fucking-believable!

"I would like to ask you if you have anything in your vehicle that I should know about?"

I shook my head, "No, sir."

"Do you have any sums of money in cash totaling ten thousand dollars or more?"

"No, sir, I don't."

"Do you have any illicit substances? Cocaine? Heroin? Methamphetamines?"

"No, sir."

"Do you have any marijuana?"

"No, sir."

"Do you have any weapons? Firearms? Explosives?"

"No, sir."

"Well, I'm happy to hear that, Mr. Allen. So you wouldn't mind then if I were to just take a quick look in your car?"

Un-fucking-believable!

This moment was not my life flashing before my eyes, but it was something akin. I learned very clearly in that instant that believing that something will never happen to you does not prevent it from happening. Then I imagined the call to my parents from jail. I thought of the happy days of liberty I had experienced throughout my youth, and the coming decade that would be my life without freedom. I noted the feelings in that exact moment where my choices were still mine and I could practice all of the freedoms for which I had become a part of the marijuana culture. And now here I was on the brink, pushing freedom to its limit. *Prepare yourself, Benjamin. You made these choices. Just play it until the end. That is all you can do now.*

"Well, to be honest sir, I really don't think that is necessary. I've been honest with you and I don't have anything to hide, so I don't think you need to look in the car... I have to say no."

The mood suddenly took a heavy turn. It became both more menacing and less intelligent. The officers demeanor shifted instantly and his voice tensed and adopted an accusatory tone, threatening. "Well if you don't have anything to hide, then why do you have a problem with me looking?"

His formality had fallen away almost instantly, and he seemed like a brutish child who had just been told he couldn't have dessert until he finishes his meal. The power was mine.

"Pardon, sir, this is a stressful and intimidating situation. I have never had this happen to me, and I feel a little bit like I am being bullied, and I am really cold. So there is no reason for you to look in my car, and I feel like it is my responsibility to say no to you."

The muscles around his eyes indicated that behind his dark shades his eyes had narrowed. A smirk appeared on his face. "I think you have something in your car. When you first rolled the window down, I was pretty sure that I could smell marijuana..." he paused for dramatic emphasis, "under that orange you had just peeled to cover the scent!"

This was pathetic, and he and I both knew it. He was using a tactic that he had learned in his training. It was played too late, and there was absolutely no smell that was escaping those dry-bags. I fought back my own smirk.

"Sir, I have no idea what you smelled, but there is no marijuana in this car." I instantly pictured the forty pounds not a foot away from us.

"You are going to have to let me into your car so that I can see for myself," he retorted.

"Really, sir, this is inappropriate. You can't search my car, and I won't change that answer."

He looked at me. He was angered by this. We were standing on a frigid, ugly stretch of earth and everything they had told him to do during the workshops wasn't working.

"We are going to stand here until you let me into that car, because I think you are carrying marijuana."

How long was it before he decided to call for dogs? Would I break down if we just stood there? My mind would snap, it was already close. The reality was his suspicions were correct, and the truth has a way of coming out. This was Mormon country...

He was watching me, waiting. I threw up a Hail Mary. I looked him directly in his aviators. "Sir, I am a good Christian boy, and the only drug I need in my life is Jesus."

The longest moment of my life ensued...

"You are free to go."
I stared for a second. His face was as stolid as it had been previously.
"Ok, thank you, sir. Have a nice day. God bless."
That was an immature parting shot and I knew it. I walked to my car and got in. I didn't dare look back. I was waiting for him to rap on the window, to change his mind, to keep me until the dogs came. Then I heard his car turn on. I tried not to shake as I put the papers away. He hastily pulled off the shoulder and only thirty feet ahead crossed to the other side of the freeway on a dirt track, then raced off back towards Oregon to reclaim his spot, to resume his hunt for the vile and the wicked. I didn't stick around to watch. I glanced over to the passenger seat. Paranoia was laughing with ecstasy. The trip was his, and he knew it.

8

The moment I pulled away, I felt like the luckiest human alive. And then, after the adrenalin dissipated ten minutes later, the fear gripped me. I still had the entire country to cross, and now I had the very real understanding that it was possible to be caught. I wasn't just another car on the road. I was a young man with West Coast license plates driving across the country in the winter when it was undoubtedly cheaper and safer, and much, much faster to fly. And nobody in law enforcement was unaware that it was the end of the growing season. Once I was driving again and my mind had time to think clearly, my calm act, which I had so valiantly assumed for that moment of greatest importance, disintegrated, and all I could think about was the reality of my situation. I was looked for, hunted.

The minutes and miles ticked by and my heart rate hastened with the hopes that if it went faster, so would the drive. But it didn't. Idaho and Utah passed like haunted years. In Wyoming, I broke into a cold sweat when I saw a navy-blue Suburban with government plates and white letters reading "Task Force" printed boldly on the side. He was just over the border and I gulped in relief when I saw he was on the phone and distracted. I didn't stop.

I holed up in Cheyenne and spent the next morning at a car rental place spouting off some invented story about how I didn't think my car was equipped for winter driving and I wondered if I could trade it in for something more appropriate to the Midwest? *Maybe with Wyoming license plates.* The man looked beleaguered and finally told me there wasn't much he could do. He asked if I wanted to file a report. I said no, tried to smile, and walked out. It was late and there was no avoiding the car. My heart rate increased again.

The moment I crossed the border into Nebraska, two unmarked navy blue Suburbans entered the freeway from an on-ramp and settled in behind me. They had government plates. I tried to pretend they didn't exist as my heart banged at my ribcage trying to get out. Eventually they shifted lanes and passed me. I saw men in aviator sunglasses staring at me from both vehicles. *Oh God! They are looking for me!!* I wondered if the paranoia was causing me to hallucinate. There seemed to be nobody else on the road, and the sun was shining on me like a spotlight. My cherry red car glowed, and the sun said, "That man in the red car. He is the one you want."

I pulled over at a rest stop to breathe. I was about to hyperventilate, and I still had most of that day and at least two more full days to go. I looked on the GPS for alternative country routes, but then I thought I would just look more out of place, and would have to reduce my speed.

That afternoon, a Nebraska state trooper drove up behind me. He came out of nowhere, way too fast, and then stuck to my bumper for the next two miles. Sweat squeezed out between my hands and the steering wheel, my mouth felt like it was full of chalk. He passed me and I pretended to be singing along with whatever music happened to be playing, Britney Spears most likely. I acted as if I didn't notice him. Fifteen miles up the road, I passed him. He had pulled over a bearded young man with California plates.

I made it into Iowa and the temperature plummeted. By the time I reached Iowa City, it was zero degrees and I had an odd, spastic heartbeat.

Temperatures remained that way the next day. The thermometer read one degree and never changed. In Illinois, I was followed briefly by another state trooper, but nobody wanted to get out of their car when it was that far below freezing. I got into the hustle of Chicago traffic and, for the first time since my close scrape with incarceration, I began to think I could make it. Then, in eastern Ohio, I ran straight into a lake effect blizzard—it was a whiteout. I crept along, trailing the brake lights of the car in front of me, and suddenly I found that I was in a town. There was no possibility to continue that day, and I sat in the lobby of the hotel with the other waylaid travelers and watched the news. The blizzard raged through the night, muting the clamor outside, but doing nothing for the agitated clamor in my head.

9

It was day six and I had yet to hear from Raptor. In fact, I had not had familiar contact since leaving Portland. Not a single person knew where I was.

The snowplows passed mid-morning and the hotel emptied, following the plows down the freeway. It was icy and a frightening number of cars had ended up in the ditch.

In Pennsylvania, a semi-truck slid off the shoulder and its trailer had tipped. The police were there and somehow I felt more at ease. As long as I didn't crash, I was pretty sure law enforcement had other things to worry about. "This is the last stretch, Ben." I told myself "You can make it."

As I continued east, the weather warmed, the snow dissipated, and the normal driving pace resumed. I was going to make it to New York by dusk. But that made the next problem far more pertinent. Where was the call I was waiting on?

I stopped near Easton, Pennsylvania, and decided to make the call myself. I was only two hours from New York, and that was going to be a world of its own. I couldn't get into the city with nowhere to go. I picked up the yet-unused track phone that I had kept within reach the entire drive. *All right, Raptor. Let's see who the East Coast connection is. You'd better pick up the fucking phone.*

He did.

"Yo, Sup?"

"Uh, is this Raptor?"

"..... ... Ooooh shyiiit! Uh, yeeah man, this is him!"

His voice was the epitome of a stoner. It was nasal, and every vowel had a Y attached to it. I tried to stick to business. "I've been expecting a call from you, but I'm two hours outside of New York and I didn't want to wait any longer. So I want to know where to meet you."

"Nyew York? Ah shyit, nah, man. Why you going to Nyew York? You gotta go to Boston!"

I let the information settle in and then felt a slow rage bubble towards the surface. "Ok, Raptor, if I am supposed to be in Boston, then why was I told to go to New York?"

He could hear the menace. "Ah… ah, dude, that's my byad. Shiit man, but it's totally chill, just go to Boston instead. It's noo problem!"

I had a mental picture of the asshole on the other end of the line. Greasy hair, pale, uncut fingernails. Immediately I hated him.

"You realize that Boston adds several more hours of driving? Crossing more state lines? In the dark? Why am I just finding this out now? I've been on the road for six days. It's not very *chill* and I have been expecting an address in New York. I don't really like to hear that I am going to a different city. It makes me feel like I don't know what the fuck is happening! And that's not the way this should work."

I realized that I had no idea who Raptor was, maybe a stoner, maybe a goon with a gun, but I was angry and couldn't withhold my words.

"Ok, I will go to Boston, but I need the address where I am going to meet you."

There was a pause. "…Well, I'm… I'm not actually in Boston right now. I'm in Arizona…" then he sped up, sensing that this was not favorable news. "But I'm gonna call my guy and he will definitely meet you! Everything is totally chill man."

I tried to remain calm. "So let me get this straight. I'm not going to New York; I'm going to Boston? And I'm not meeting you, I'm meeting someone else? And do you know where I am meeting your *guy*?"

He blurted his response. He knew he had fucked up. "I just gotta call him, man. He will be there, definitely. I'm super sorry, bro, syuper sorry, I just forgot, er, I just didn't realize you were getting there so soon. So head to Boston, and I will call him and then call you back with the meeting point."

"Fine," I growled. "Just make sure there is someone waiting for me in Boston." I hung up.

The extra, unexpected miles made the drive feel interminable. And, despite the diminishing distance to Boston, no call came.

I reached Boston and should have felt some relief, but instead I was driving into a city I had never been to and I had no idea where to go or who was waiting for me, or even if someone *was* waiting for me. I spent a stressful half-hour lost in a tangle of freeways and exits and finally emerged downtown. I simply drove until I saw a parking space and pulled in. I tried to make myself breathe. It was eleven at night and not a word.

I forced myself to calm down, and picked up the phone again. It rang for a while, then Raptor finally picked it up, launching himself into a speech about how the guy was supposed to be there, but he wouldn't pick up his phone, and he had been calling for hours, and he was still trying and I just had to "chill out, man," and... .

"So, there is nobody here waiting for me, Raptor. I don't want to carry this stuff anymore. You understand this is a big risk for me, right?"

"Shyit dude, ok, just give me one more hour. I'll find him, I don't know what the fuck he is doing."

"And if you don't find him?" I asked.

He was uncomfortable on the other end. "I guess you get a hotel?"

"Just try to find him." I said. I was weary.

I sat in the car and looked around. I was in a daze. I had been concentrating on just getting to the East Coast, and in the six days of driving, I had hardly considered that something might go wrong when I got here. How wrong might it go? I tried not to think about it.

An hour passed before I got a call and it wasn't from Raptor. I was expecting his idiotic equivalent, but the voice did not advertise such a thing. It was calm and straightforward.

"Hello, my name is Courtney, I just heard from Raptor that you are in town. It sounds like you have had a long drive and there was some miscommunication about meeting on this end. I didn't expect anyone, but it is no problem. I will come and meet you and we can easily sort this out. It will take me about 45 minutes to get across town. Is that ok for you?"

My temper was still short and I was still uncertain of the whole organization, and I couldn't avoid being a bit sharp.

"Yeah, man, that's ok. But I have spent a lot of time waiting today, and I am pretty ready to get out of this car. So don't leave me hanging."

He chuckled. "I understand."

Then he gave me instructions. He asked me to plug an address into my GPS. I would drive there and park on the right side of the street so that I was facing west. Eventually, a man wearing a hooded jacket would walk into the light of a streetlamp and light a cigarette. Then he would get into a car. I was to follow that car.

I shivered. The instructions made everything about the engagement seem sketchy and dark and dangerous. I glanced to my right and caught sight of Paranoia looking smug. He winked at me.

I began to wonder if it was some kind of setup. Would they rob me? Kill me? Was it the police? Had it been planned from the beginning? Should I drive away, hole up in a seedy hotel and call my boys on the farm? What were my fucking choices? But something in Courtney's voice was reassuring. And I was within sight of completing my task. I had made it to the end, seemingly against the odds. I turned on the car.

When Courtney gave me the instructions, it sounded like another moment in my Hollywood movie, and I didn't think that it would transpire as he had described it. But it did... exactly! I sat for about thirty minutes, and then a man with a hood over his head stepped from the darkness and into the soft spill of the streetlight. He lit a cigarette. He took a long pull and then crossed the street to a car. When he drove away, I followed.

We drove for ten minutes and stopped on a fairly nice-looking street of townhouses. The man got out of his car and walked towards me. I got out.

He extended his hand. "I'm Courtney. You must be exhausted. Let's get your bags inside. You can relax and we can talk somewhere comfortable. What a long drive. You did a good job!"

10

The apartment was in the process of being painted, and Courtney apologized for the smell. He pulled a cloth cover from a couch and invited me to sit down. He disappeared into the kitchen and came back several minutes later with a mug of tea. I realized that it was nearly one in the morning. I didn't have any clue how this part went. I had understood that I would simply leave the bags with Raptor and then depart, but I felt like I was sitting down to a business meeting.

Courtney asked me about the trip. I told him it was long and that the weather had been bad, but I left out the other details. As we talked, I could tell he was studying me, trying to figure out who he was dealing with. I was doing the same, and I couldn't figure it out. He certainly didn't seem to be Raptor's lackey who was just doing a favor. The man was in his forties certainly, and he was clean cut, and a bit hip, sporting a soul patch below his lip, and an earring. He was very composed and pleasant. Otherwise, I could tell nothing about him. But Courtney must have decided a few things about me. One: I was harmless. Two: I had no clue what I was doing. And three: I was reasonable enough to work with.

"So do you know who I am?" he finally said.

"Well, as far as I understood, you are Raptor's friend and you were meeting me since he isn't around." I said this, but I already knew this was not the case.

Courtney nodded his head. "I see. Ok, I'm going to tell you a quick story about what I do."

I sipped my rooibos tea.

"Back in the nineties, me and some friends organized a business. At that time, a lot of herb on the East Coast was coming in from Canada. We developed a safe system to get it into the country and disperse it along the coast. We usually flew planes over Lake Ontario and dropped loads of about one thousand pounds into the lake. There was a jet boat on location to retrieve the load and drive it to the US side. Once we had a few of these dropped loads, we had Home Depot trucks and packaging, and the load would be labeled as office supplies and driven to Boston. We had our schedule pretty well organized and the truck would arrive at a Home Depot store. Depending on cameras and shifts, there was a window of about twenty-five minutes when distributors from along the East Coast could pick up what they needed. My part of that business was dealing with all the money that came in and went out. So… that is my line of work. I didn't expect you today because Raptor didn't tell me that anyone was coming, but forty pounds is not a big deal. That is something that I can easily deal with for you."

I didn't have anything to say.

"Now Raptor… do you know Raptor?"

I shook my head. "No, he is a friend of a friend I guess, and I thought he was sort of, well… you."

Courtney nodded with a pleasant smile. "I'm going to tell you who Raptor is. Now, he is a nice enough guy, pretty easy-going, all right to be around at parties. But Raptor doesn't understand this business."

Courtney's pleasant mannerisms dissipated and he became a bit more matter-of-fact. "I'm going to be a little blunt with you right now. Raptor wanted you to think *he* is *me*. And he wanted that because it allows him to pretend he is the guy who is going to sell your product. But all Raptor would do with your product is bring it to me, and take a large cut. In this case, he didn't even take the time to come here, and I expect that he still wants a big cut. He kept information from you and me, which puts us both in danger, and he did it to take advantage of you because you needed him to get to me."

I still didn't have anything to say.

Courtney promoted his smile again, "So, Raptor is a decent enough guy sometimes, but I don't include him in business deals."

I contemplated this. "So, what does that mean for this situation?"

"Well, I want to make a deal with you. And I want Raptor out. If you guys decide to pay him something, that is fine, but this transaction has to be between your side and me. If that doesn't work for you, it's no problem."

I understood that part clearly. It meant I would take the bags, put them back in the trunk of the car, and go on my merry way to god knows where.

"Well, I am not particularly fond of Raptor. I don't think he has done anything to help me. Kind of the contrary. And I don't love the idea of him making a bunch of money off a deal that he did nothing for, but, it's really not my call to make. I'm just a delivery boy in this situation, you understand? Can you give me a little time to make a call to my guys? They have to make the decision."

"Of course!" he said with his reassuring smile.

I dialed the other number in my phone: Tennessee.

Nick was groggy. He'd been sleeping and didn't get overexcited when he heard my voice, which was better.

"Listen, we have a weird situation here." I gave him a recap of my conversation with Courtney. "So, what do we do? Do we cut Raptor out?"

Nick grumbled for a moment. "Well it sounds like he is trying to get in on a deal without doing much, and it sounds like he isn't really on top of things. He was our connection though. I dunno man, you are there. What do you think?"

"Well, I don't know where else to go with this stuff for one, and I don't really want to just cruise around with it. This guy here seems to be the person who was going to deal with this stuff in the end. I don't know how this business works, but it seems like we should make the deal." I realized I was speaking in a hushed voice, even though I was sitting in the car and I didn't need to. There was a moment on the other end. I could hear Alden whine sleepily.

"Ok, make the deal, I guess. As long as we are getting forty two hundred a pound."

"Ok. Got it. Sorry to wake you up."

He chuckled. "Glad you are all right."

Courtney and I took the bags into the basement. He removed several locks from a heavy door and we walked into a room. It was wall-to-wall with weed. I had never in my life seen so much pot in one place. We unpacked the bags and he made notes of the strains and inspected them. He told me it would be some days before money came, which was as I expected. We discussed contact procedures in case I was the one to retrieve the money, and then we shook hands and I asked him the quickest way out of Boston towards New York.

"I have to get out of here, I said. The stress is getting to me."

11

As I drove away, I thought of the guys on the farm and how simple things were there. I realized that we were just naïve farmers in Northern California. Here, marijuana was still a drug and it was bought and sold by drug dealers.

No money came in during the following week, and I flew home on Christmas Eve. Somehow, along the way, Raptor became the money courier. Nick and Jonah never managed to get all the money from him. I continued to have panic attacks every time I saw a cop car, and I can only assume that the Idaho state trooper felt like he did the right thing to a good Christian boy.

Book Three

Part 4

1

One morning in early spring, I woke to my phone ringing. It was Logan and he didn't wait for my hello.

"I have terrible news. Tempo murdered Brooke yesterday, and then died trying to escape."

The numbness of shock washed across me with Logan's surreal words. Nothing in my brain worked.

"You should just come over to my place," Logan said.

I hung up.

The next hours were confusing and emotional. So were the next two weeks. It took a long time to wrap our heads around the horrid event because nobody seemed clear on what had happened, and many refused to believe that it *had* happened.

I relived the quiet times in the Tipsytom cabin where we had all spent hours together laughing and joking. I had lived so intimately with both of them, known them well. It didn't seem possible. Brooke was so passive and gentle. Tempo was so thoughtful and playful. I also thought of the last time I had seen them in the fall. Brooke had been distant, and Tempo had been himself. The only thing remotely negative that I could recall was when Tempo said Brooke wouldn't stop moping because his girlfriend was pressuring him to have kids and he wasn't ready— hardly indicative of a personal grudge. What had changed in four months? What had happened between them? What had happened in Tempo's brain? Insanity was the only thing that, ironically, made any sense to me—that Tempo had gone fucking crazy.

When I thought back to Tipsytom that first year, I found I was heartbroken losing both friends, and I couldn't bring myself to feel anger towards Tempo. I couldn't imagine him in any villainous light, and I didn't want to accept the facts. But, the facts were unavoidable.

Logan and I discovered the first day that Brooke and his girlfriend, Kathleen, had been murdered by Tempo at Kathleen's house in Cougar Springs, the valley north of the Tipsytom, and that he'd attacked two other people with a knife—people who had arrived at the scene and saw the victims. Then Tempo fled the valley, chased by the police. According to the report, Tempo lost control of his car and crashed into a tree. He was killed instantly.

Beyond that, there were rumors of an outraged ex-lover taking revenge, and that the victims had been stabbed to death. I was skeptical.

"Imagine how Lena is doing," I said to Logan.

He looked miserable. "God, I know. She lost her lover and her best friend, and the media is suggesting that Tempo was jealous of Brooke's girl. That's a load of shit."

We attempted to go on with our lives, but for three days after the incident, we couldn't stay focused and would eventually just sit around feeling anxious and repeating the facts over and over again while Logan put down beers.

"I can't fathom what Lena is going through. That poor sweet girl... Is there any way in this universe that she and Brooke had something? And Tempo was—"

"No," I said. "No fuckin way in any dimension. I think it had to have been something between Brooke and Tempo, or it was a setup." I dearly wanted to believe this—that there was some foul play at work, some explanation that would clear Tempo's name. I hoped it would come to light that there was some sinister third party involvement, some ugly, unlovable goons. But as the facts gradually surfaced, it seemed as though the ugly goon was our friend.

2

Brooke's memorial service was a dazed event held in the little woodland town in Oregon where he'd grown up. It was mostly attended by his childhood community; only a handful of us were there from the farm. The event was very sad, and everyone seemed to have an opinion about why and how the tragedy had occurred. They needed to understand.

Some blamed the industry that Brooke was involved in and said it attracted outlaws. Others, who knew Tempo, said it had nothing to do with drugs—it was a crime of passion. Others backed the conspiracy theory. One girl was requesting information she could use to undertake a personal investigation with the hope of proving that something big was missing from the evidence.

Brooke's parents sat quietly and mourned the loss of their son.

Lena sat amidst a close group of protective friends and cried throughout the entire ceremony. I suspected she'd been in that state a great deal since the devastating crime.

We sat with Jona on the steps of the Commons where the ceremony had been held. There was no smile on his face, but he was calm and clear as always.

"So do you know anything else?" asked Kay.

Jona sighed. "I had to go identify the body. The police somehow found out that I was Brooke's land partner and the closest person who could legally identify him. So I drove over the next morning and saw him... It was brutal."

My heart sank as Jona continued.

"Brooke was beaten pretty badly. His face was swollen and, well, it was definitely Brooke, but he didn't look like the guy we know. I will try not to think about that when I remember him." Jona looked down at his hands, which were placed palm up on his knees in a meditative posture.

3

I apprehensively told my parents about the tragedy.

"I won't allow you to go down there again!" my father enjoined.

"This was one crazy and terrible event. This stuff never happens down there," I defended.

"But it does! This is terrifying, and you want to go back and be around those people?"

I didn't have the heart to get angry. "Those *people* are my friends, and they are just people, good people. Something unknown happened, but this event isn't because of the weed industry. This could have been anywhere. Bad stuff happens all the time all over the place."

My father was grave. "That place down in California, and that work, is a magnet for bad guys. You are out in the hills and the work is illegal. There's a lot of unchecked money floating around. You don't think that draws people who want to get something the easy way? Who don't care about the people there? You bet your ass there are guys down there who would rob you and probably kill you. And they might even seem nice when you meet them!"

I couldn't completely argue this point. The case of Brooke and Tempo was exceptional and outlandish and rare in any situation, but the marijuana trade certainly did attract those on the fringe. A place where one could make good money tax-free. There was also a lot of cash exchanged in a remote part of the country where law enforcement was far away and people were isolated. People could be very vulnerable, and there were stories of robberies.

The previous fall, Mara had told me of an incident in the notorious area known as the Traces, a stretch of land near Lassy that had been divided into acre plots with practically no water available. The Traces was entirely occupied by upstart pot farmers. Mara had worked there for a time and knew of an incident at one of the neighboring farms where armed men arrived at a trim scene wearing ski masks. They duct-taped a handful of workers to chairs, and robbed them of everything they had. Sadly, that wasn't the only story I'd heard.

But we looked out for one another on the farm, and we did what we could to pay attention to who we were working with. There were many eccentric people, I'd met them, but there was vigilance too.

Tempo was a guy who had been relatively normal; been a friend. There was no way to predict that outcome, no matter what was going on. I couldn't blame the industry. In terms of the good and the bad people, the sub-culture I was part of was just a shrunken-down version of society at large.

"Well, sometimes, the situation allows the bad side of people to come out," my mother said.

I could tell she was hoping to avoid a fight.

"I met Tempo with you that time in Eugene, and he was very nice. He gave me a big hug, and I liked him. But maybe that shows that an illegal business, where there is danger and risk, makes people take chances, and creates mistrust and easy opportunities to do something bad. Lots of people out there are opportunistic, especially if they see a situation where they can get away with something. If someone is already acting outside the law, isn't it easy to go further?"

I knew very well that people took chances in the business—I had learned that only a few months before on my drive across the country. There were opportunists and those influenced by the pressure and allure of money and gains. And if your risks are successful, then it could be tempting to take the next step and abuse the fragile structure of a young society. But I wasn't convinced that growing pot was a gateway activity to becoming a murderer.

I shrugged. "I just can't condemn a whole culture based on one sad, isolated occurrence. I know a lot of people, and by far, the good outnumber the bad. It is a young world and it is kind of the Wild West, and maybe bad things happen. But really, really good things are happening too, things that are not happening in other places. People are putting new ways of living into practice..."

My father got up and walked out of the room. My parents weren't fond of my tirades on changing cultures.

I spent the rest of the day wondering if I was naïve and blinded by my interest in adventure. Maybe I was part of a dark scene that enabled villains to do wrong and turned good people into criminals.

4

It took six months for Brooke's case to close. I was only two weeks away from making the journey back to Tipsytom for the autumn season when Kay sent me a link to the police report.

The crime had been premeditated by at least one day. Surveillance footage from a store showed Tempo purchasing a taser, handcuffs, and ankle restraints. Then he drove down to Cougar Springs where he tortured Brooke and Kathleen. The bodies were found with plastic bags duct-taped over their heads, their ankles tied to a railing, and their hands cuffed and tied to a rope that ascended to a pulley on the ceiling. They had taser wounds. Kathleen died from strangulation. Brooke died from blunt force trauma to the head and strangulation. He also had electrical wire and rope tied around his neck.

Kathleen had somehow managed to escape just long enough to make an emergency call. The records indicated that she managed to plead for help, but no other information was communicated. The regional police department notified the nearest neighbors, who went to Kathleen's house to make sure that everything was ok. One of the neighbors, Mary Hanes, went inside and was attacked by the man who they later identified as Tempo. He held her down and slashed her throat with a knife. Hearing commotion, Mary's husband, Burt Hanes, entered the house. Tempo attacked him.

Burt's wife, wounded but alive, fled and escaped in the car. Tempo used the taser on Burt and stabbed him in the throat, but Burt was able to wrestle the knife away from Tempo and escape. As he ran, he saw Tempo getting into a car and leaving the scene. Burt and Mary managed to reconvene, and although injured, were able to get to a store where the police were notified and medical assistance was initiated.

Meanwhile, Tempo drove towards the coast. His car was recognized by a policeman and a chase ensued through the windy backcountry. Several police cars joined the chase until Tempo reached Highway 101. He drove south, pursued by a law enforcement vehicle until he lost control of his car and crashed into an oak tree. He died from the injuries sustained in the crash.

In the car, the police found receipts for the taser and handcuffs. They also found a large sum of cash and packaged marijuana. It was determined that Tempo acted alone. It was stated that the motive of the crime was believed to be related to the sale of marijuana.

5

I was eating dinner in Nick's yurt. Alden was bouncing on the bed and Carmen was chasing Granit, their new addition to the family, as he tottered across the floor. The cozy little room bloomed with life. Nick was smoking a joint and we were talking about my adventures on the East Coast. We didn't really know if the trip was a success or not because a lot of the money still hadn't come in, and the guys weren't feeling too optimistic about it. Raptor had it.

"There are just too many hands involved," Nick said, and stared at the smoke drifting towards the ceiling. "Too many people we don't know. I think I would rather sell it for less here, and deal with the people I trust and like. Keep it safe for everyone too... Fuck man, I almost wish Brooke had been arrested on his drive. Maybe he would still be around."

Jona looked up. "It's interesting you say that. I heard a rumor that Tempo took some weed to Atlanta for Brooke and Kathleen after the incident when Brooke got busted. Word on the street is it didn't go right. Tempo lost the weed, or was robbed, or something."

Nick looked at him. "So what?"

Jona was relaxed but his eyes were full of fire. "If this has any credibility, it sounds like Brooke basically demanded the money, blamed Tempo for the loss. I never really liked Tempo, but Brooke could be stubborn, and when money gets involved, lots of money, crazy shit happens. I don't know, though. I only know that Tempo had been working for Brooke before it happened."

Nick contemplated the smoke again. "It's such a lovely plant." He smiled at the haze forming in front of his eyes, his big face ruddy in the soft light of the room, cheery as Santa Claus. "Just trying to get medicine to the people."

Jona nodded. "It's a harsh reality to accept that maybe in the end it was about drugs and money. It's a hard world out there."

Nick didn't take his eyes off the drifting thread of cloud sailing past his cheeks. "Do you think Tempo ran into the tree on purpose? Killed himself when reality caught up with him?"

Jona sighed. "We'll never know what happened in that guy's mind, before or after."

I watched the kids jumping around, jabbering and laughing like two chubby wolf pups. "So what changes?" I asked.

Nick stopped watching his smoke and looked at me with a smile. "Nothing. We just live our lives. We just try to do the right thing, Benji. And we just keep going."

6

Brooke's mandolin and an old radio he sometimes listened to sat under a tree in the cedar grove where he had forgotten them, probably to run happily down to the creek for a swim, or to wander off into some beautiful daydream. Nobody ever moved them. Nobody wanted to take them away in case he ever came back looking for them.

Book Four: The Nature of Gardens (Fall 2011/Fall 2012/Spring 2013)

Part 1

1

I pulled an armful of colas from the wire where they were drying and unceremoniously dumped them in a large plastic bin. I moved down the row and collected additional armfuls, occasionally stopping to pry apart a particularly dense bud to inspect it's innards for grey or yellow or pink fuzzy mold.

"Thank god the Mr. Nice doesn't have any *botrytis*, guys. We don't need another situation like the Pineapple Train Wreck."

I heard murmurs of assent, but couldn't see who was speaking because I was ensconced in a forest of hanging marijuana.

I was hyper vigilant about mold after the first large harvest dried too slowly and we were obliged to spend three days sorting and cutting out contaminated buds, often entire colas. We had to re-trim ten pounds of finished product, reducing it to eight pounds, a five-thousand-dollar loss when all was taken into account.

I deposited another batch into a bin and then counted the

containers. Ten. I looked around at the magic wands suspended from the wires crisscrossing the room—they worth a hundred thousand bucks at least. And these were just the ones in the yurt where we dried overflow buds that couldn't fit in the dry rooms. And I was tossing them around like hay. Well, it was my job, and very normal by that time. I hardly took the time to marvel anymore, there was too much to do.

"Ok, guys, how close are you to finishing the Fire? I have the Mr. Nice bins prepped and ready for you. Great looking buds, not really any larf, and they are pretty dense. We should fly through this stuff. I think you'll be happy with it."

There was a distracted cheer. I moved out of the jungle and looked at my crew.

They were all absorbed in their work, chipping away at the little green nuggets with their tiny scissors, a series of calculated snips and into the bag of finished, uniform, little green globs of plant matter. They snipped like a well-oiled machine, mechanical hands, scooping the buds from the tray, finding the little "crow's feet," and cutting the stem flush, sprucing the calyxes so that the ganja didn't appear like it had been ground down by a weed whacker—"mowed" as we termed that poor form of trimming in the industry.

Their unresponsiveness was a good sign. I didn't like to disturb the trimmers when they were in this mode, when they were most productive. I silently moved around the table inspecting their work. They were listening to a podcast on intestinal and colon cleanses. I'd noticed that this group had a curious obsession with poop and had held many passionate debates on the hue and morphology of feces, and what feces might indicate about the health of the body. They were a hard group to feed because all of them had demanding and inflexible diets. Rainy lived exclusively on chia seeds, almond butter, and algae. Doug required seven lemons every day and two bars of dark chocolate. Maria Luisa guzzled buffalo milk like a newborn calf. And Jordan was on a strictly liquid regimen supplemented with colloidal silver. Each year had its thing.

I pulled a bud from Lydia's bag and twirled it around, I could see her shoulders tense slightly—nobody enjoys it when the boss inspects their work, not in any industry.

"Looks, good, just make sure you're cutting the stems short and straight, otherwise they poke holes in the bags."

Lydia's bin was nearly empty. She was the fastest trimmer, a native Californian only twenty years old. But she had been trimming weed a quarter of her life. I often used her as a marker to determine the ease with which the strain of weed would be processed. She could easily trim two pounds in a day if all the conditions were good. If it was lots of little buds ("popcorn") or the loose, fluffy, lower stem buds we called "larf" that had no density, then she might be down to a pound, and the others would be closer to three quarters.

"When you are ready, you can go ahead and grab one of the Mr. Nice totes, Lydia."

She smiled up at me "Thanks, Benji!"

I had adopted the approach of distributing the weed into bins, dividing the bigger and smaller buds evenly between them so that there was no issue with cherry picking. It was one trick that ensured peaceful relationships in the yurt, but it was hardly necessary compared to the previous year. This year our trimmers were as agreeable as lambs.

"Hey, Dori, a lot of these buds could be broken down further. You are leaving too much stem. They should be more or less down to their smallest unit, then they are nice and uniform."

Dori jabbed his thumb into the air. "Sure thing, Boss! I got it!"

I always felt stupid telling them the same things over and over, but if I didn't, the trimming invariably became sloppier.

I pawed through Constantina's bag. She was the sloppiest and also the most combative employee—a fiery Andalucían with a princess complex who preferred not to be managed. There was a lighthearted war between us. I removed a handful of semi-trimmed buds from her bag of finished product and put them back on her tray.

"These are pretty loose, can you clean them up?"

She stopped trimming and grabbed one, looking closely at it. I pointed out a number of crow's feet she'd missed. "Just get those, and take a look, you didn't trim whole sides on a bunch of those...."

"Si, si! I know, I know!" she rolled her eyes "You are so picky!"

"We aren't picky here, Constantina, we are very forgiving. There are some farms that make you cut each calyx, and each little sugar leaf down the middle so that the buds look bigger, and you can only handle them by the stem so that you don't break off any trichromes. Life could be worse."

I looked in her jar of littles, the ones she deemed too small to trim.

"And half of these are easily trimmable, you know that. You should have hardly any popcorns since we are doing them all with the trim machine."

I held one up for the group. "Remember guys, if it is big enough to be a bong load, we trim it."

Constantina scowled.

"Thank you, I know it's a pain in the ass, but that is how we sell the stuff and make money."

I didn't feel like explaining our policy yet again, so I went into my office to check on the curing process, wondering how I ended up with a job that felt so, well, job-like, with employees who complained and bosses who critiqued. As the industry became increasingly certain of legalization, many farms began to attempt a more professional approach. We had hardly become professional in the Tipsytom Valley, but I was managing the final product and that required standards, regulation and, however we could, making our production more efficient. Sometimes I missed the Wild West atmosphere of the previous years. I'd become involved in the side of the farm that was more about business than community, culture, and lifestyle. But the business side was necessary for the existence of the others. My role was essential.

I looked around my office—a six-by-ten-foot box with canvas sides, a plywood roof, and the old door from the cabin. Mara and I had built the structure inside the yurt and shoved it against one wall, and then called it an office. I spent a great deal of time interred in the little pretense of a room, rifling through endless bags of finished and unfinished marijuana—weighing, sorting, inspecting, and relocating from one bag to another. On the table were scales and plastic bags, a vacuum sealer, scissors, a magnifying glass, a large lamp I could move around for accurate lighting, and papers with numbers and names and everything incriminating: the farm's records for the year.

On the floor were bins of weighed pounds, ready to be shipped out, and piles of extra materials for trimming: oil, alcohol, trays, scissors, paper towels, rags, and various other accoutrements. Against the walls were makeshift shelves lined with labeled bins, and one with rows of paper bags nested in plastic bags. It was on those bags that I focused my attention.

Once the weed was trimmed, it required curing—essentially an adjustable storing process to ease the product to the right degree of dryness in order to retain the utmost flavor and redolence. If the weed was too wet, it would be exposed to air and stored in paper bags that drew the moisture out. If it was too dry, I would seal the plastic bag around it. I was constantly checking the state of the buds, squeezing them, smelling them, and generally coddling them. I began to transfer a batch of cured OG Kush into turkey bags, preparing to weigh them into individual bags of 456 grams—a pound plus a couple of grams for the buyer to sample without losing weight when it was divided into smaller quantities for sale.

I opened a turkey bag, which was named as such because the original intention was to host the carcass of a turkey while it roasted in an oven and excreted juices. It just so happened that this grade of plastic partially muffled the smell of the weed, was relatively durable, and almost perfectly accommodated a pound of trimmed cannabis. I wondered on occasion what the sales teams of various oven bag manufacturers imagined when they reviewed their sales statistics from around the country....

"Dear Lord!" one dumpy analyst would express, then re-examine the numbers with a shudder. "The folk in Northern California must be decimating turkey populations! It's grotesque!"

Another would shake her head in dismay. "I don't understand. We can't keep the stores in stock! Is it humanly possible to eat that many fowl?"

"Per capita, each individual in the region has to eat a whole turkey every two days to go through that many bags!" the CEO would say, with a growing sense of unease as he looked at the unprecedented sales of oven bags.

The spokesmen from the sales committee would push his thick glasses up his nose and stutter, "W...w...we presume it is some form of b...b...black magic cult that is sacrificing h...h...horrendous numbers of turkeys between San Francisco, California, and Eugene, Oregon."

The CEO would pause and regard his agitated team like a good leader, wiping the sweat from his brow. "We have agreed that the best course of action is to ask no questions and to increase distribution in the area, especially in small rural towns where it appears the cult has the deepest hold... God save them!"

I managed to weigh two pounds before there was a knock at the door. I had learned that uninterrupted work time maxed out at about ten minutes. I invited the visitor inside, and poured two glasses of wine, pretending that I had comfortable facilities in which to offer drinks, and that my office wasn't simply a feeble partition from the rest of the yurt.

Dori entered. Dori was a Quaker-raised Pennsylvanian with a crew cut. He was a mid-America, corn-fed, straight shooter. It made no sense for him to exist in the industry, which made me appreciate his presence all the more.

"I have four topics of discussion, Boss."

I had never been comfortable with the formal way he addressed me.

"I want to weigh out my Fire Kush... because I am done. Trimmed it all." He waited for my approval.

"Cool, great. Start on the Mr. Nice."

He nodded solemnly. "We need another bottle of rubbing alcohol out there. My snips are sticking to everything they touch." Dori paused again, standing at attention. His mannerisms had appeared contemptuous to me in the first days of his employment, but it was just because he was traditional... and sarcastic as hell. Sometimes it was impossible to tell which was which.

"K, go on."

I grabbed a bottle of alcohol from under the table and handed it to him.

"Thanks, Boss. And the people want something sweet. Their blood sugar is low."

"All right, I can probably find something," I said with a grin. "And the last thing?"

He nodded. "I believe you have mail in the Questions And Comments box."

The Questions And Comments box was a manila envelope pinned to my door. The team had installed it with the intention to abuse me. It was a sign of our expansive comfort with one another because nobody needed privacy when discussing matters of import. If a complaint came in that someone was getting away with poor trimming, or that someone was receiving special treatment, or that someone was unhappy with the consistency of their feces, this issue would be vocally and publicly discussed. After six weeks together, we had no secrets and no reservations. So mainly, I received anonymous love letters and questions about my preferred breast size, or a scrawled message advising me that the smell of my socks was overpowering the scent of the marijuana.

The new message was a request to take them on a field trip to my living quarters, a cruel joke, as they knew I was a prisoner to the yurt and slept on top of my office when I had a spare moment for niceties like sleep.

The yurt offered several benefits—but free time was not one. By living there, I was a guardian of the trove. I could stoke the fire, and ensure that the drying weed was managed. I could be found in case of emergency or non-emergency, as was more often the case. And frankly, I was bad at choosing campsites—like cougar dens and compost piles. The yurt was also appealingly warm. So I spent my nights inhaling the sweetly intrusive aroma of cannabis and dreaming of flowery nymphs and purple dragons.

"You are all invited to my abode if you can trim your way

through that enchanted forest," I said, emerging from my office and pointing at the dense drapes of drying weed that surrounded my sleeping quarters. I produced a couple of dark chocolate bars and set them on the table. There was a chorus of pleasure. Humans are often most pleased by simple favors.

This group was less dramatic than prior trimmers. Or maybe it was simply that after a time, the company of strange characters and social renegades became normal. They were simply *people*, like everyone else. When I stopped and considered them as individuals, however, they were all fascinating. Most of them were artists of some persuasion, or ardent travelers, or devotees of a craft who found they could work hard for a small portion of the year and buy themselves freedom to pursue their passions the rest of the time. They were people who, I felt, represented a large part of the industry and the culture—annual migrants who valued and relied on the opportunities ganja provided because it was not a permanent commitment. They could run off to chase their hearts and dreams after serving a few months trimming weed. These people were the most free—propagators of the cultural ideologies, travelers who exposed ideas to the masses that had never even heard of the cannabis culture in the west.

I sat down to pick ganja leaves and stems out of my socks while watching the trimmers casually sharing their life stories and information, subtly shaping each other, and all learning their way through the slow minutes. It was trim camp. It was life school.

I worked at the black mass that had been the soles of my feet. Everything I owned was coated in resin. I found plant matter in the most unpredictable of places. I could wash my clothes three times, and still a faint odor of weed loitered. When I visited my parents, my mother would demand that I strip in the garage and bring me old, untainted clothes to wear before she allowed me to enter the house. The removal of the crust on the bottoms of my feet was futile, but it was one of those satisfying obsessions and challenges. I liked to peel an entire footprint of resin from the soles of my feet—intact. This rarely happened because everything nearby was attracted by the magnetic quality of the incomparable stickiness that increased as the material was handled. By the time half the resin cake and plant matter was removed, my fingers were like Velcro and had acquired string, paperclips, and candy wrappers.

Doug finished rolling a joint. "Okaaaay, guys! Who wants to get high?"

There were some polite declines.

"Nobody?" His voice was crestfallen, although he had expected this response.

Most of them didn't smoke, or if they did, it was a rare occasion. I'd noticed over the three years of the farm's existence that most of the trimmers were not regular smokers. They'd just shrug when I asked why.

"I'm not here because I love to get stoned. It's the other things the place offers that are more appealing."

Workers came with various perspectives on weed—from ardent love of smoking, to respect for the plant's power as a medicine with little interest in personal use, to a cash crop that allowed them to pursue their interests. I'd been surprised at first by how few were, according to my definition, "potheads" or daily users, but by this point, smoking or not smoking was just a topic that nobody really discussed. All attitudes were normal. I accepted that the draw of the industry was far beyond the draw of the plant, no matter how unique and tantalizing its properties.

"Hmm, nobody wants to get high? How about stoned?" There was silence.

"Nope," Rainy finally responded.

"Ok, goofed? That's what they do in South Africa. Blazed? Lit? Baked, keyed, ripped? Get irie, as the Rastafarians say? No?" Doug lit the joint. He was a performer at heart, a singer from Burlington who enjoyed dressing and acting like a hippy because it was a fun character to play. "Okay, Rainy. I did words for being stoned. You name all the words you can think of for weed!"

Rainy was a retired gutter punk, an extremist who eventually discovered the comforts of moderation. She was the partner of Ryan, Brooke's younger brother. They had come to the farm so that Ryan could understand his brother's world and make peace in his heart.

Ryan was silent and gentle, and though he trimmed and worked, he spent a great deal of time walking around and discovering the land, or talking with Jona or me about Brooke's favorite places to loiter and the locations of his activity. But day-to-day, he and Rainy were just part of the trim table, which Ryan said he wanted.

"It is all part of what my brother was doing. Living in this scene and participating is how I can get closer to him."

Doug stared expectantly at Rainy.

Rainy looked thoughtful. "Well, there have got to be a million words for weed and for smoking. Let's see… Well, cannabis and marijuana. Let's start with the official words. Weed, pot, grass, ganja, herb, hmm, bud… uh, maryjane, Buddha… Damn, why is it so hard to think of them?"

This game was new and entertaining. The trimmers were always ravenous for new activities at the table—there were only so many podcasts they could listen to before their brains atrophied from lack of creativity.

"Chronic!" said Mara, who was trimming that day.

"Cheeba!" added Jasmine, an intellectual girl from

Massachusetts who had followed her nomadic sister west for a few months on a lark and ended up in the Tipsytom Valley.

"Endo!" said Gavin, the blond Welshman who Jona had met in a drumming workshop and invited to come with his Mexican partner, Maria Luisa. They both had a quiet demeanor, which added to the general calm of the year.

"Puro! Or Mota," added Constantina.

"Brassicus!" said Dori.

"Really? Brassicus? That's a new one." Lydia looked skeptical. "How about nugs, or reefer?"

"Wacky tobaccy, and sticky-icky-icky!" It was Hunter, who had just come in from the weather and was kicking off his boots. "Or shwag."

Doug shook his head, "Nah, shwag is shitty weed. It's a specification of quality."

"Oh that's bullshit!" rejoined Rainy. "It's still a word for weed!"

The talk broke down into an argument over the specifics.

Hunter went to the corner where we had a music area full of things to strum and bang on, and began to squeak out some noise on a harmonium.

"Who wants to jam tonight?" Hunter called out, looking at me with mischief on his face.

The word "yes" was emphatic and multiple.

"Hunter, you saboteur, I am looking for a pound each from these guys today. We gotta go until eleven at least. Don't you know we have hours these days? A schedule to adhere to?"

I was teasing him because he knew very well we would all quit with the slightest excuse. Half the job was managing the weed, and the other half was managing the people. We had to keep them happy, and leisure was the best way to prevent emotional breakdowns from excessive work hours. Otherwise, I donned my counselor's hat and spent hours listening to woes and distress, and trying to be compassionate and patient. Problems arose regardless, but if we made efforts to keep the trimmers happy with treats and playful activities, and read stories and sang songs to them, they tended to forget their unhappiness, and work was easier for everyone.

"It's set then!" he announced. "It is Jona's birthday, and Benji and I are going to dress in drag and sing to him!"

My eyebrows arched in surprise, but there was no escape once the idea had been put forth. I glared at Hunter, who smiled broadly back at me.

"It's your job to keep them happy!" he reminded me lovingly. "You gotta make sacrifices."

2

Thick and gruff, Nick's hands lifted the arching arm of marijuana that bent down to greet us with surprising delicacy. He studied the dark purple buds with the prudent eyes of a doctor. We were crouched in the garden amid arboreal monuments, discussing our strategy for the remainder of the season.

"I want to take ten pounds to town tomorrow. I'll take eight of the Blue Dream that's already vacuum-sealed, and I want to take a couple of the Fire Kush if you can make sure we have cleaned up pounds without any shake in them. Maybe vacuum seal them tonight. There's a guy on the coast who's interested, a new guy. I'm hoping he'll like them and buy them all."

It was an effort to find consistent buyers, especially late in the fall when everyone had harvested and the market was saturated. Nick had been taking samples and small amounts every couple of weeks, keeping a constant income at the farm, and trying to secure a large buyer.

"Prices are the lowest I've ever seen right now—lucky if we can get twelve. Some people are selling pounds for eight hundred. Part of me wants to bury it all and save it for the spring when everyone is dry and desperate. I'm pretty slow to learn all these bootlegging tricks, I guess."

Nick grabbed another cola and pried it open, then gouged out a large section and cast it to the ground. "Mold! All of these late harvest strains seem to lose about five percent of their yield," he scowled. "No consistency with black market trade, Benji. I'm ready for them to legalize it. I'm sure all the big corporations will get involved, and maybe it will be taxed and regulated, and become tricky to get a growing permit, and all that bullshit, but the prohibition days aren't as fruitful as they used to be. Too many people doing it. The prices have no stability. It's hard for the farmers—we just have to sell it for what they offer. Then you feel pressure to really go for the bootlegging approach and ship it to the East Coast for more money and, well, you know how that is. Almost go to jail, and don't know the people you are working with. Fuck, we are still waiting on that dude from Arizona, whatzis name? Raptor?"

He petted the plant and smelled it gingerly. "I just like growing the stuff and making people happy, providing medicine, ya know? Yep... ready for this prohibition to end."

Nick plopped down and the ground trembled in an effort to hold his form. His trademark smile boarded his face. "Wow! We have so much, though! So much to be thankful for! We can feed our friends and our families and manifest amazing gatherings of high-power people."

He grabbed my arm and shook me to remind me to be thankful and I winced and was thankful when he relinquished my arm.

"Everything is great."

Nick looked through the vegetation at the land he had made his home. "Spirit provides." He lit a joint and yanked another spot of mold from a broccoli-like bundle of buds.

Voices reached us and we spied Joey and Diego, two of the farmhands, moving through the garden.

"They are attracted to the smell of this delicious Lavender!" Nick beamed and waved the joint in the air. "Yoohoo! Over here!"

Following their noses, they waded over.

"Not many places left to hide. The garden is mostly gone," Diego said as he received the joint with a bow. He was a regal Texan of indigenous heritage, an easy-going personality, and a hard worker. Joey was a stocky, curly-haired specter with sparse, prematurely gray facial hair. He had a knack for lurking and a dominant tendency towards paranoia. He was a character I had expected to meet years before in that community—skittish, reserved, untrusting, and certain that the government was one short step behind him. Joey told me he had buried caches of provisions and tools and various supplies in hidden locations between Texas and Alaska, including several shipping containers replete with generators and gasoline and seed banks ample enough to start food forests.

"There's gonna be a big collapse soon. I mean really big. Could be any day," Joey would mutter. "I'm just trying to fly under the radar and be prepared."

Diego handed him the joint, and Joey gave an unrequested report—he was always succinct and formal when he talked about work.

"Solar panels are back in business, so we are completely off the generators again. Benji gave me the numbers from the Fire Kush littles we ran through the trim machine: 2,088 grams. We processed all the Jack this morning. Wasn't much of it—219 grams. The first

Diesel we harvested is in hoop house number two, rows C and D. The trim machine is fucked up again. I think it's the drive shaft. I'll take it apart this evening and try to fix it."

Nick responded hastily. "Maybe I'll come look at it before you take it apart. We don't have too much left to get through, right? All the Blue Dream is in the dry rooms, so it is just this Sour Diesel, those few Ambrosia plants, and whatever leftover buds that are still scattered around the garden, which I'm not too worried about. Those will probably be for a head stash anyway."

Joey and Diego nodded and Nick scowled again. "I don't know how that fucking trim machine keeps breaking. They are really simple, and for the amount we paid for that thing, it should last a lifetime, not half a season. That piece of crap was almost ten grand."

Every tool related to marijuana production seemed to be marked up ten times what it would be if it were used for blueberries or carnations: custom scissors, trimming trays with kief screens in the bottom. Everything was absurdly expensive, and the trim machine was simply a steel grate with a sharp-edged fan beneath it that removed all the plants' fan leaves and any other plant appendix that extended too far from the main body. We had been using it to trim little buds not worth the time of our trimmers. The result was not as nice as hand-trimmed buds, but it was passable.

I had seen other trim machines on friend's farms. One model was a big tube with cheese grater teeth that gnawed the buds into ruffled little balls. Some farmers were happy enough with the product that they were willing to call it a finished product. Some said trim machines were the future of the industry and that the need for human trimmers had an expiration date. If the machines replaced trimmers, it would undoubtedly save farms large sums of money, but what would be lost? It was an innovation, and could be a major turning point in our way of life. Although the machines were just another tool, many people grew uncomfortable with the prospect of what the trim machines of the future could mean for the community. It was a divisive topic.

Heaving himself towards the sky, Nick stood and surveyed the rest of the garden. It was largely skeletal.

"Just two sativa strains left. Those strains love to take their time. At least there hasn't been much rain this year, and all the Indica is down. Shit, we are almost out of here. I think we should harvest a little of the Sour Diesel now. If you look at the trichromes, they haven't turned foggy. It should make a nice heady high. We can keep some for personal use. The rest we can give another week, but let's stop giving them the nutrients and flush them with water."

Reaching into his jacket, Joey produced a large test tube full of cloudy liquid. He glanced nervously to the side, certain that agents in dark suits were watching from the trees.

"Do you guys want to drink some Ormus? It's a mineral compound, the bare essence of life. The forces of darkness don't want us to know about it... but I know. It will make you feel more alive."

We all looked around, trying to catch a glimpse of the dark forces in the trees, then we drank the Ormus.

3

Mara was making pies in the kitchen, with pears harvested from a feral garden she and Jona discovered at the foot of the valley, one of those hidden traces of the civilizations that graced the Tipsytom over the ages and then disappeared like all civilizations do. Mara had won the war of the women and was Jona's partner, though he still confided in me that he was not averse to the idea of polygamy.

"I mean, if I can provide for them? Or we can create what we need as a family, what's so wrong with that?"

I-told him to give it a shot. "Life is an endless experiment."

Pear pie and pit-roasted goose was the menu for Jona's birthday. Carmen and Pelli were buzzing around the kitchen herding their brood in front of them. Ezra and Alden were naked and hatefully destroying walnuts with a hammer. Little Granit was wobbling in uncoordinated bewilderment as toddlers do.

Since Nick had brought his family to live on the farm, and built a second yurt, the domicile had largely shifted under Carmen's purview. The cougar-haunted wilderness took on a domestic feel, and rules had been set down. The trimmers even had daily chores of cutting wood, cleaning the yurt and, though it had been immediately disrespected, there was a stipulation that nobody could smoke ganja until after dinner. With little ones running around, it had become a family farm.

"The boys have been yammering all day about going on a tractor ride, Ben. Can you just drive them down to Carmen's house or something?" Pelli pleaded "They're little terrors and we aren't going to eat until midnight if we go at this pace."

I corralled the naked imps and told them we could go destroy some blackberry bushes instead of walnuts. They cheered and made horrible faces that only five-year-olds can produce.

Carmen had Granit under an arm and was skillfully cleaving kale with her free hand. "Oh, Benji, if you are down at our house, could you kill a couple of geese?" She smiled warmly "It would be a huge help. Oh, and maybe get the sweat lodge started, or tell Nick to do it. Thanks!"

The boys were easy to please. We trundled and lurched down the new road we were in the process of building, toward Nick and

Carmen's yurt in the cedar grove. I tore a couple of stumps out of the ground with the backhoe arm, which maddened the boys who delighted in power. I too enjoyed the immense power of the tractor and often laughed maniacally when I recalled our feeble assortment of ailing tools from our first year—straightening nails to build the shed and using our screwdriver as a spatula handle. Now, only two years later, we had a tractor with a bucket and an arm, and we could make roads in a casual afternoon just to entertain the children. The boys laughed wickedly. I joined them and wrenched another stump from the earth.

Claiming that I had spied a gnome down by the creek, I sent the boys in pursuit and finished my babysitting shift for the day.

4

Geese are wary creatures—they sensed my sanguine intention as I stepped into their enclosure and they gathered together for support. I wished I was collecting chickens, but a bear had torn the chicken coop to pieces and exterminated the population. Although the geese waddled and griped awkwardly, I was very aware that they were dexterous beasts. Opting for surprise, I sprang forward and attempted to corner a plump old dame, but she out-maneuvered me. I lunged for a young gander, but he backpedalled and feinted left, sending my tackling arms in the wrong direction.

I hailed Joey, who was trying to slip away to some guarded stash where he'd been tucking away survival supplies. He joined my cause, but seemed not to trust the geese. Jona caught wind of the event and came in with a low, wide stance. The muttering geese stomped around, deftly outsmarting us at every turn, although we dove and slid and tumbled over them. Hunter added to our ranks and we created a wall. A nasty, ill-tempered goose hissed at me mockingly. Ready to abandon the idea of fowl for dinner, we held hands and formed a barrier, and with a desperate dive, Hunter blindsided our victim and pinned it against the wall.

"Let's just have one goose for dinner," opined Jona with deep breaths of exertion.

Jona produced a kukri blade and I pinioned the bird's legs and gripped its head, stretching its neck across a log. Jona stood a moment in silence, giving thanks for the life of the bird, and then we both took deep breaths. There was a thick noise as the head separated from the body and then a burst of commotion as the corpse tried to take flight. I held its feet as the wings beat and blood spurted from the sheared neck. The bird smote the air in its final journey and then slowly came to rest. We stood in silence for a time, impacted by the gravity of the moment and the power of the creature, feeling sheepish that we had been so light-hearted about its capture when it was fleeing for its life.

"I think that was its soul flying away," Hunter said solemnly.

I took the bird to Pelli and Carmen to pluck, and then headed down to the field past the vegetable gardens where Nick had parked his mobile sauna, a trailer he outfitted with a woodstove and cedar benches. Joey, Diego, and I split kindling and got a fire going.

"We are living the life here!" Diego rejoiced. "I feel so free and so in control of my existence! Farm-raised geese, fresh veggies, and wild pear pie for dinner, then a sweat and a plunge in the creek! I feel like the king of the world."

Joey hushed him and looked at the sky. "Man, I've told you that you gotta talk quietly. They have little flying robots that are just too high for us to see, but they hear everything. If you keep the volume down it helps."

Joey always whispered.

Diego's smile faded. "Man, nobody is listening to us."

Joey's laugh was grim. "You can tell yourself that, but they are. They are everywhere, man, you can't escape them. The best thing to do is not draw any attention to yourself."

We heard a rustling in the bushes, and we all jumped in alarm, brandishing logs and axes. But it was just Melvin, Dori's dog. Melvin had gotten hold of someone's unguarded stash and eaten a quarter ounce of weed three days prior. He was not "good old Melvin, the chipper lab" anymore. He staggered from the trees, and stood before us trying to grasp what it all meant. I had never seen a dog sweat, but Melvin's brow was beaded with perspiration. He stared at us, his tongue oozing to the ground, his clouded eyes begging the infinite questions of the universe as he struggled through a troubled enlightenment. He swayed slightly, then stiff as a board fell sideways, and gave in to the grips of the drug.

Diego looked from Melvin to Joey. "You think he is one of them?"

Joey regarded the Labrador with suspicion.

5

Though it remained only half a town, Tipsytom had modernized somewhat to meet the needs and interests of the new community that had become the dominant population. Dori, Hunter, Mara, and I were in the new organic food grocery, an improbable success in a town where two years prior it would have been run out of town for selling non-foods items like vegan mayonnaise and Tofurky. We were there to buy the oxymoronic, organic, non-GMO junk food we all craved after our kale and quinoa-based fare. No matter the interest in the pursuit of more wholesome lifestyles, the surreptitious joy of a corndog, or candy bar, or some other maddeningly delicious and unhealthy treat from mainstream American society had to be indulged on occasion, sometimes frequent occasions.

"Ah look, Reese's Peanut Butter Cups that aren't actually Reese's! And they are organic!" Dori exclaimed, guilty with delight. "It must be much healthier than the name brand!"

The door opened with a jingling of bells and a rustling of Tibetan prayer flags. "Oh, those are delicious. I was going to buy some of those myself."

I recognized the mesmeric voice of Raj Ras. He moved knowingly through the store, picking up bags of gluten-free cookies and corn syrup-free soda.

"You know there are about ten times more people in the valley this fall than there were last year?" Raj's conversational tone was not particularly convincing as he studied the ingredients on a canister of organic cheese spray. "Ooh, great, no artificial colorants! I just want to hide from all the foreigners, but they keep coming by for incense, so I end up meeting them all. Strange new crowd! They all seem so, well, normal. It feels like the community here could just be any other town in America."

I looked at him with unveiled skepticism and he approached the topic from an alternative angle while juggling several bags of sweet potato chips.

"Ok, I know, it's not like any old town, but it is a bit more mainstream... like, the lifestyle here has become more accepted. And it certainly feels less wild and more settled... and in a way, more boring." He chuckled. "You know, it would be great if this community became the norm in society, or if less adventurous, more conservative people showed up and participated in the culture. It means that good ideas are spreading elsewhere and attracting people. We are less frightening now than we used to be.

The laws aren't keeping people away. More people have tried it and been successful. The uncertainty has diminished, so it seems natural that the more mainstream people are coming. It's not bad at all—we can show off all the groovy ideas we have here!"

Raj seemed satisfied that he had made his point and bowed to me, dropping a bag of pretzels. "Om mani padme hum!"

We made for the new bar that had elbowed its way in between the gas station and the fire department.

"So you think it's all just mainstream American society here, folks?" Dori asked with loud and defiant amusement. "We just more o them Mericans?"

Mara had been contemplating these questions after hearing what Raj Ras had opined. "Ya know, I am not from America, but what I see everywhere is zat we aren't so different from any other place in the end. There is just a higher likelihood of certain values and certain activities here, but we still have the same diversity of peoples, the good, the bad, the smart, the dumb, as in our larger parent societies—America or Germany, or wherever. If we think zat *we* are so different here, that creates an *us and them* feeling and we close off to anyone who is different. I came to this place to escape that exactly. But is the same old failure to change that happens everywhere.

Dori looked annoyed, "But hasn't it changed? Don't you see more folks like *me?* Don't dress the right way, like to watch football and drink beer, ya know?"

"Well, it is always changing—this culture always has, and it has always been diverse, so nobody really dresses the right way or acts the right way. There are certainly more people, but it doesn't matter if they watch football or not. Maybe they vill find something different and they vill change. Like Raj said—the values here are spreading and attracting people."

"Hmmff," Dori replied. "Or it's just easy money and they don't care about the *values* at all!"

Mara shrugged, "They are still exposed to the ideas."

The bar was called Shooters & Shooters because it sold liquor in front and guns in back—an enlightened invention of Tipsytom's old guard. Sandy, who had been the barmaid at the Tipsytom Tavern during my first term in the valley, and her boyfriend Bart, were the new proprietors. The old cast from the tavern relocated in solidarity, leaving the Tipsytom Tavern a lonely, quiet sort of woodland bar. They had even plundered the Star Trek pinball machine and relocated it to where it could continue collecting dust in a new milieu.

Although it was just mid-afternoon, a crowd of young trimmers gathered at Shooters. This group had recently arrived in town, but they were a rowdy and vibrant bunch costumed in clothes that seemed to have been purchased from a toyshop rather than an apparel store. We entered into a conversation with a black kid from Alabama named Bables.

Bables wore a grimy lion's tail hanging from the back of his belt, a bed sheet, and an alien antennae headband. He was anything but normal. He ranted for a time about his trip across the country in an old motor home with fourteen of his fellow "road dogs." He spoke of their anger at a society where they didn't fit in. Some of his fellows were dancing and shrieking madly at the jukebox. Two locals in the corner looked nervous.

I ordered a beer from Sandy, and like a good local bartender, she had a comment on the strangers.

"More and more of these new types coming in. Don't seem to get the customs here. Not so much respect for the way we do things."

I laughed. "Wasn't I one of those just three years ago?"

She shrugged, "Well, I dunno. The new wave seems different. Like it's their right to be here, or like they own the place."

It was the story of the callous invader. I had been waiting to hear that comment in Tipsytom for years. The same had happened with my wave of immigrants a few years earlier in the Lassy area, when I'd first heard those fears expressed. I had been the subject of those concerns. The locals in Lassy felt the shift in power as multitudes of strangers moved into the area. As the newcomers swelled in numbers and their lifestyles infringed on the old timers, they were regarded as a threat. And now the same had come to the Tipsytom Valley. It didn't matter if the newcomers were different or not—*normal, mainstream, crazy,* or *weird,* the old community was not the strongest group in the valley anymore. My wave, which had become integrated into the community over time, was in the middle. We were potential allies. We had arrived during a different phase. We had been considered more of a curiosity than a threat, and now we were familiar. But we could be pulled to one side or the other. We could represent the locals and make them feel stronger, and observe the strangers as *frightening others,* or we could represent the next wave of our own kind and overwhelm the locals, making the valley work according to our desires. My hope was that we would do neither. My hope was that we would be a bridge between.

Hunter pulled up a stool and imbibed his beer in one long pull. "It's kind of hard to say who represents this subculture, isn't it? It's everyone and no one. The locals were something else before the farmers came. The farmers were something else before they mixed with the locals. And each new wave brings something new. No individual or sub-group gets to define the culture."

I followed his example with my beer, and Hunter gave a broad smile. "There is certainly a chance that this weird little social experiment will become increasingly undefined and directionless. Maybe that holds potential greatness. Let's get the hell out of here."

6

I perched on the hill and spied on the activities below. The tired sun of early winter surrendered a meek warmth that was snatched away by a cold and greedy wind. From the hill, I could see the yurt, the cabin, the beach, the gardens, and all the various work facilities. Closing-down operations were underway. The trimmers were relaying baggage to their cars down by the vegetable garden. Jona was dragging the skeletons of the once-proud and expansive cannabis plants to their pyre. He heaved them one at a time onto the pile with brutal caveman strength. The stalks tangled and strained to flee the hill, but there was no life left in them and they quickly surrendered to their fate. Nick was sprawled on the beach asleep, preparing for hibernation while his toddler clambered on his belly. Hunter and Mara were decommissioning the yurt, sweeping the evidence of activity into dustpans and throwing old sheets over the stories of the season. No smoke curled from the woodstove in the kitchen, and the rumble of idling car engines announced that it was time to hit the road and move on.

I had paid everyone the previous evening. We were all tired, ready to leave and had run out of things to talk about. Some were happy; some were upset. Some grumbled that they made less because they trimmed at a higher quality and were slower. Some couldn't resist commenting that there had been a lot of lightweight weed—that we didn't have big buds like at the other farms where they'd worked and where they could get through two pounds a day.

The same complaints were heard on every farm.

I recalled the time when I was in their position—the first year in Humboldt—and feeling as though I hadn't received the money I deserved. Now I understand it from the opposite position. There were no guarantees in the industry. After months of giving all your energy every day, I wondered if any amount would seem like fair compensation.

Some opted to take their payment in weed if they had a connection to turn the weight into a larger profit. Joey and Diego were sending boxes to Kentucky with the US Postal Service and doing quite well for themselves. Dori was going to risk a drive to Phoenix where he could triple his earnings with one exchange. As I handed each person an envelope or a weighed bag of buds, I felt the strange separation and cool distance that commerce forces between friendships. We all tried to smile, and I forced a hug on each of them. They were a good group, a mellow group. Maybe the next season wouldn't be so tranquil. One thing I knew for certain was that stability was still a fragile and vague idea on the farm.

As I watched the people move like ants preparing for winter, my thoughts drifted back to a story I'd heard a couple of nights before. Carmen and Nick had invited Jona, Mara, Hunter, and me for dinner at their yurt. They'd also invited Gerald, a friend who occasionally came out to the farm to lend a hand. He had his own small grow operation at his house outside of Arcata and had run into unexpected troubles.

"I don't even know how I pissed off my neighbors, but I am pretty sure it was the guy next door," Gerald said with a perplexed pass of fingers through his hair. "That guy is the only one who knew I had a crop. Either way, someone called the cops and told them I was growing, because they said they had received an anonymous tip that I had marijuana in my yard."

Nick slapped the table with a hearty laugh. "That's why we live out here where the neighbors can't even hear us!"

Gerald shrugged as if to say we couldn't all live out here. "So, one afternoon, the police knock on my door and they tell me about this anonymous call and ask to come in. Naturally, I asked if they had a warrant. They laugh and one of them pulls out his iPhone and gets on Google maps and zooms in on my yard. *'Looks like you have about twenty plants here, Mr. Getty. We don't have a warrant, but I promise you we could have one in fifteen minutes. Now we don't even want to see your plants, we just want to come in and talk.'* It goes something like that, so I show them that I have my medical script and all that, and the cops tell me that it doesn't matter because they can bust me for illegal structures or agriculture in a residential zone, or something like that. They also said that if they get a complaint about someone, they pay extra attention to their movements and you know what that means. They will wait and bust you when you are making a sale, and then they really can fuck you."

We all sat in grim silence as Gerald relayed his tale, reflecting on those suppressed fears that lay beneath the surface of the farming community. The fears that we pushed down deep because it wasn't worth the stress to consider them every day. We knew they could appear any day as an odious reality.

"Finally, I asked what they wanted, I mean I was kind of confused, ya know. They are saying all of this stuff, basically threatening me, but they aren't there to fine me or arrest me or cut my plants down. And the one guy is like, *'Ok, you have two options. We can come in and cut down all your plants and give you a fine. That means you not only make no money this season, you lose money, or... You keep growing your plants and the police department takes half of your profit.'* I was just like, What the FUCK, but there was nothing I could say. I mean, it is my whole income for the year."

We were all clenching our teeth.

"So you had to take the deal, I guess?" Jona finally asked.

"Yeah man, had to. So now, I'm getting robbed by the corrupt fucking police department. They said they are going to decide the value and someone will let me know at some point, and will collect the cash from me. I don't know, weird sketchy shit. And I don't think there is anything I can do. If I report them, I will definitely screw myself in the process. And who do I report them to?"

"Do you think the neighbors really called? Or maybe zee police just looked on zee maps and are doing zat to lots of people, saying somevon called," Mara said, her voice angry and suspicious. "Obviously zey are corrupt already."

"God that PISSES me off," Nick grumbled "The cops are just a racketeering organization. Organized crime at its worst—extortion."

Gerald nodded. "That's why I just want it to be legal, but it didn't get the vote in 2010, so I bet it will be a few years yet before it goes legal, maybe even a decade. Why would the government want it legal if they are just getting the money illegally and tax free?"

As I looked at the beautiful valley painted pale green and gold, and thought of the freedom that existed for me here, I wondered if I had allowed myself to be caught up in an illusion. I had come to Northern California, as had many others, because the space, and the work, and the community allowed me a sense of self-determination and opportunity I couldn't achieve elsewhere. But the reality of governance was still a dark shadow, always in the corner of my eye. We were not living an anarchic life governed by the strength and resolution of our ideals. We were absolutely subject to the laws and power of the government we live in. The wilderness of California was geographically remote and unpopulated, but at any moment, a legal entity could decide to end the subculture that had formed.

According to the federal government, our activities were illegal, and therefore liable to consequences. A disassembly would scatter the community. Ultimately, the government had control over our chosen lifestyle because the center of the lifestyle was marijuana.

What becomes of a scattered culture? It loses the traits that hold it together. But the important part of the cannabis industry subculture has already worked itself into the veins of American society. The traits that were unique to the remote growing community might not last, but elements and ideas and stories were floating around the world with the individuals who had been involved. The community had lasted long enough for ideas of an alternative reality to take hold. It was a culture of silent action.

Maybe the subculture I was part of could serve its purpose for only a short time. It was a conference of cultures that didn't want the attendants to stay. It was there as a host until the lessons had been well learned and the ideas shared, and then those participating needed to return to live their new values in a place where others would witness them. The ganja country was a place to experiment and discover, but it was also an escape from the reigning paradigm, and not all the young and restless and disenchanted peoples of the world could escape to it. Many had to stay in their homes and make the changes they wanted to see from where they were.

There was a reason why the subculture was so transient. The marijuana industry was just one good footing for a movement to rally around during its ascent. It was a schoolhouse, a place to prepare and get strong. A gathering that broadcast the fact that many of us were looking for something different.

I decided not to go back the following year. I determined that I had learned what I wanted to and that it was time for me to be another of the transient legions participating briefly in the great experiment, and then moving on to the next step, whatever that might be.

Book Four

Part 2

1

I couldn't escape.

"Hey, Benji, I'm at a farm in southern Humboldt," Logan said and I could hear his grin over the line. "Could really use your help for the harvest."

Once you get into the scene, it can be hard to get out. Your network grows, the work is absurdly lucrative, and every time you commit, you know that it is for just a short time. You will be free again in the blink of an eye with a pocket full of cash.

Trimming had become such a common occupation that it seemed I had few friends who didn't make the trek to California or southern Oregon during the fall to give themselves a financial boost for the rest of the year. It was widely talked about and hardly considered extreme, or adventurous, or outlandish. For many of the seasonal trimmers, it was just a fun and social couple of months with good pay and good food. For many, it didn't require any change in lifestyle—it was just a valuable enabler of whatever lifestyle that person wanted to live during the rest of the year in their respective communities.

After five years of change and evolution, I no longer perceived the industry in California as a hidden subculture where brave pioneers of social change and bold rebels gathered to live out their dream. It was no longer a Brigadoon in the mountains that a lost dreamer might stumble upon. It had become something different— abundant work that fit the lifestyle of a generation afraid of long-term commitments and who understood that social acceptance of marijuana on the West Coast was no longer a contentious debate. For all practical purposes, the pot prohibition era was over.

I frequently received e-mails and phone calls from friends and acquaintances, or the friends of acquaintances asking if I could get them a job. Some of the older retired folks from my community had even started to work with scissors at a trim table—it was work nearly anyone could do. I sometimes wondered just how many small farms there were scattered among the folds of the mountainous tract from Eugene to San Francisco, and beyond.

"Thousands. I've heard numbers of fifty thousand farms between Oregon and California," Logan said as we moved through the garden loping off colas from the gargantuan plants. "There are like seven-hundred-and-fifty-thousand people with medical marijuana prescriptions in California. A lot of people want weed all the time, and pretty much everyone living around these small towns is a grower, or involved in weed in some manner. It's a billion-dollar industry, man."

I took a closer look at the crystal-covered plant that was so highly desirable, while Logan rambled on.

"And even though Cali has a ton of farms, our community of farmers in this part of the world is just a small part of this whole weed industry. It's totally global. The online community of people trading genetics, seeds, growing equipment—it's endless. There are people working with this plant in every respect from medicine to products, and the ways they are finding to use it are increasing all the time. We are just one group in a network of many others connected by herb."

I looked around the farm. We were carrying plants into a straw bale barn to dry. There were a handful of improvised structures and makeshift facilities. The property had the look and feel of most farms I'd been on. There was a house through the woods where half-a-dozen people of various origins were trimming. They seemed a lot like the other trimmers I'd met over time. I knew the house down the road was busy at the same task, just like the one beyond that.

We heaved a tarp laden with highly valuable plant matter into the barn and began to hang it on wire cables.

"I mean, think about how many different ways this plant has become a part of society. There is our weird little group of farmers and trimmers out here in the hills, and then add the people who grow some indoor stuff all over the country, and then the different levels of sales all the way down to the dealers on the street. A lot of those guys we may not relate to at all, but we are still connected to them. Their lives and communities are built around the plant too. And there are the activists and doctors who work to legalize and prescribe it. And shit! There are all the people smoking it! We are just one of the groups tied to the great green gift!"

Logan paused and walked into the sun to look out across the emerald hills. He sighed and studied the landscape with concern, as one who beholds a face they have seen their whole life, but finally notices something imperceptible has changed—something so subtle that there is no visible sign to acknowledge.

"So many people are affected by one plant," Logan continued. "There have been people in these hills farming for decades. Imagine the changes those older farmers have seen. Every couple of years things are different. Just ten, or maybe fifteen years back, it was a handful of nervous types hiding from the law. Now they are part of a thriving community changing America. And before long, it might all change again. Legal, recreational cannabis is on the ballot in a handful of states. It's bound to happen soon, and when it becomes legal, well, marijuana will just be another crop with regulations and taxes and all that stuff that won't allow for these people from around the world to gather. There has been so much exciting growth with this community... and probably it is moribund, doomed to expire before it ever finds a moment of stability."

Logan sighed. "What's happening right now... it will go away with legalization. That will be the death knell. And already people are preparing for that change. Makes me sad."

2

In the spring of 2013, I was in Tipsytom packaging pounds with Jona and Hunter because I couldn't stay away from there either. We were in the cabin that was now a warm, insulated, dry-walled home with a real door and hardwood floors. We sat around the bins full of ganja chatting and unconsciously measuring out units of marijuana, as if we were peeling potatoes.

"So what are you gonna do when they legalize this stuff, Jona? Are you gonna trek off into the hills and trap beavers?" Hunter chuckled at his own comment and Jona's expression indicated he had heard no humor at all in the question.

"No, I need to think about my family. That wouldn't be fair to them. I'll stay right here. This is my home. I don't really see why I would leave even if weed becomes legal. I'll just keep farming. Maybe the money won't be quite as good, but farmers can make a living."

Jona continued with his work having said all he needed to on the topic.

The cannabis movement was different for Jona, who understood the way things were in those parts as normal. He didn't live in multiple worlds. This was his existence—in the wilderness, unbounded by the walls of society, at one with his environment, occupied with basic human needs. He would always live this way because it was the way he knew how to exist, and whether there was ganja or not, he would not change.

"What about you, Hunter?" I asked.

Hunter came from a background like mine. He had stumbled upon the lifestyle and found that it suited him. He was aware that the lifestyle we'd known might end soon.

"I don't know," Hunter said with uncharacteristic simplicity. It was the answer I heard most often. There were a lot of people aware of the looming possibility that their economic means, as well as their lifestyle, might be approaching a precipice.

"It's not like pot farming is going to end, fellas!" Jona said as his hands worked their way around the buds.

"Yeah, but you will have to farm differently," Hunter replied. "You can't employ guys like us, or at least not twenty of us like you used to. You will have so many new expenses, you won't be able to afford it. Besides, these people won't come, not if they have to pay taxes, or if they get lower wages. You are going to lose the people who come for money, and with it you'll lose the people who come for the community. You are right, pot farming isn't going anywhere, but this form of the industry will change. This morphology of things with seasonal workers and the concentration of people with similar goals and values will change. But legalization isn't just going to change the economic aspects of your life, Jona, it's going to change your whole culture. It might kill it off, or wash it so completely that the values you believe in disappear."

Jona's mouth turned up slightly with a contented smile of wisdom. "Hunter, I know things will change, and I will live and adapt as I need, but you don't have to worry about the values going away. The fact that there is a strong push towards legalization actually illustrates that the ideas of this place have spread and been accepted."

Jona picked up a handful of buds. "This plant is totally a testament to the strength of those ideas spreading. Think about this—a bunch of people who decided to live by what they thought was morally correct, even though it was not legally correct, came to this area and started to grow weed. They didn't think it was productive to fight through the bureaucracy and change the laws first, because they didn't believe in that system either, so they just went somewhere quiet and started to do what they wanted to do. They made good money, which made the risk worth it, but they wouldn't have been here if they didn't believe that it was an ok way to live. With those values, they were able to see that there are many values that may be illegal, or unaccepted by society, or just unknown, but which are actually good and wholesome. Growing marijuana is an example indicating that there are many good ways to live that aren't currently acknowledged. But look at what is happening now. People began to live by their morals, and that behavior started to grow, and more people arrived who agreed with them, and it has grown to the point where the morals are beginning to overtake the laws. Marijuana is legal in Colorado and

Washington, and it won't stop with them. That should show you that the culture of this place has grown into something bigger, and the values we just decided to live by, rather than preach, have spread by example. It reminds me to live in the way that I believe in living. You forget that we are gardeners... and the nature of a garden is that it grows."

The sweet aroma of dried cannabis filled the cabin we built with our own hands. I looked around the room. The woodstove crackled, showering light on the deerskin rug spread before it. A large salad of fresh homegrown vegetables was on the table waiting for us to take a break from our work. The soft patter of rain was dulled and pushed from our minds by the stout roof above our heads.

Nick suddenly stomped in with his eternal smile and titan presence.

"Look at these Hill-Hippy-Hip-Billies!" he bellowed joyfully. "I just got back with the clones. We have our young ladies for the next season. We are going to do it another year!" Nick's hearty laugh boomed around the cabin and he produced a bottle of whiskey and passed it around.

Outside in the Tipsytom Valley, that small vale residing humbly amidst the great American land of freedom, the spring rains fell and soaked the earth, and hopeful growth drank deeply of that fortune and prepared to break free of the ground and blossom into a new and promising existence.

Epilogue
(Fall 2017)

The cannabis industry has continued to thrive on the West Coast of the United States. In 2014, Oregon and Alaska legalized recreational marijuana, joining Washington and Colorado. And in November 2016, California, Nevada, and Massachusetts followed.

My curiosity about the changes in the community couldn't be ignored and I decided to spend the harvest season of 2017 in Humboldt County with Logan, who was running an operation.

In the four years I had been away, a great deal had transpired with the legal status of the plant, namely that marijuana was, in fact, now a legal substance, a change that gave rise to the supposition that *things* were probably not as I had left them. And since the entire population of growers and trimmers and related businesses were affected by the plant's legality, I could only assume that the curious little culture I had watched breaking from its shell had not gone undisturbed.

The farmers had been waiting years for the legalization of their crop, and always there was some uncertain speculation about the impact it would have on their lives. Now, the ink on the paperwork was drying and the changes were in motion, but lifestyle has a stubborn way of digging in its heels and defying the discomfort of transition. I was surprised to discover that to a large degree the *way of things* was still trudging along, despite the reality that a cliff and a drop of unknown distance was looming.

On a farm, day-to-day tasks are consistent in their cyclical way, and that demands stability. The farmers were still cultivating the plants, still watering, feeding, pruning, and obsessing about pests and weather. The politics might be tumultuous and unknown, but plants needed consistency. If the marijuana could not grow, then the laws had nothing to target. But the calm existence of the growing plants did not so easily extend beyond the confines of a property's borders, and outside, the interactions of humans ruled the atmosphere of the weed-growing community.

"Well, there is just a serious feeling of uncertainty. This is some peculiar in-between-phase. It's legal, but California won't start issuing growing licenses until the start of 2018, so we're still farming the way we have been," Logan responded to my questions. "Nobody knows what it will cause. We are looking at Oregon where they are stumbling through it all—recreational licenses, medical licenses, dispensaries, black market. What we see is that a lot of people are still growing, still trying to use the black market, maybe get their product out of state. But it's just harder to sell your herb. Competition is fierce and if and when you sell it... well, it's just barely lucrative anymore. Not after all the overhead... especially the cost of trimmers."

The farmers were clinging to the way things had been for one last final season—going through the routines. But there was a constant air of pessimism among the growing community and the awareness that everything they had invested in was losing value. In 2018, when the state began to issue permits, it would be the end for many of them. Most had poured their resources and money into their remote infrastructures during the era when hiding out in the hills was critically important, and now those investments were money drains. Farms were expensive to operate. Many were maintaining roads, buying water they had once pirated from streams, buying copious quantities of gasoline to run generators, and paying top dollar for quality genetics, nutrients, and all the other necessary materials needed to grow a quality crop that could compete in a saturated market. And if it got to the point where you couldn't sell your product, you were out of the game.

Farmers were selling at five hundred dollars a pound, and that was barely enough. The land they were growing on was no longer desirable real estate because the farms of the future would not be miles down rough gravel roads that had to be constantly repaired. New farms would be in accessible locations, on good, flat farmland, with paved roads and connection to the power grid.

Many farmers worried that they wouldn't have a crop to farm. They feared that assets they had invested in would have no value after the crop of 2017. The future for the farmers looked bleak. Not many seemed hopeful, and with inevitable defeat came desperation.

Farms were going as big as possible, trying for a major push that year, getting what they could while they could. There would be a money grab while there was still a lot of loose cash floating around, and then they were going to call it quits and close up shop because they knew they couldn't compete if they didn't diversify— making cannabis oil, or developing new strains. If you were just a farmer with no other outlets in the industry, then you needed scale, and that would come with a heavy price and the necessity of legality.

Yes, legal was once again an important feature of a farm. It was no longer the war on drugs that would take you down if you didn't follow the rules. It was everyone else who had an agenda, who wanted money, who took issue with some aspect of the cannabis industry. The government's new approach was not to bust the small farmer for growing marijuana, but to find everything else they had done wrong and bring in every agency available to hammer them with fines—such as illegal consumption of water, contaminating streams, building illegal structures, illegal storage of fuel, not having an adequate fire buffer around a residence, or improper disposal of waste. The list was long and the fines were hefty, and if they pinned enough of them on a small enterprising farmer, it could be enough to run him out. It meant that the farms were more closely observed by a variety of whistle blowers. Law enforcement had new allies to help shoulder the task of reigning in the illegal operations—passionate allies who had agendas of their own.

I couldn't disagree with much of this reasoning. Studies were coming out about degradation of streams and the depletion of water bodies—legitimate environmental concerns about an unregulated industry that nobody could argue was small anymore. With tens of thousands of farms, the industry had become too large to be ignored in all respects.

"I'm done after this year, buddy, regardless of what happens." Logan said flatly. "It's hard work. Stressful work. And now it pays just like a desk job. And even if I can hang for a few more years, it's only a matter of time before the bigger fish push me out of the pond."

Humboldt County always had a different atmosphere than the mountainous tracts of Trinity where the Tipsytom Valley lay. It was on the corridor that passed through the cities, was more accessible, and it was widely considered the heart of the marijuana scene. Humboldt County was the area where the disenchanted hippies chose to move back to the land in the late sixties and began to quietly cultivate marijuana under a veil of secrecy. Now the secrecy was gone and Garberville, California, was a Mecca for those who needed little more than a rumor of easy money and easy drugs to draw them into the area.

I never felt at ease when I was in Garberville. It felt more transient and a bit more sinister than the secluded hamlets further off the beaten path. But I wasn't prepared for the state of things when I pulled into town one afternoon driving the big diesel land truck we used on the farm.

It was a street party. The sidewalks were so full of people, I thought a parade was about to commence. They sat in large groups on every corner, or moved in slow, strung out gangs down the street, clearly aimless. They conversed in small clusters under the shade of claustrophobic-looking trees or leaned against the walls of grocery stores smoking cigarettes. And they watched me carefully as I rolled through town.

Sets of eyes tried to find mine, to lock, to make significant contact. Cardboard signs gently flipped up and flashed drawings of scissors. *Jesus, it's the Grapes of Wrath*, I thought to myself. These were would-be trimmers, waiting for someone to give them work. There were hundreds of them, just sitting amid their bags— napping, idling away the time, and hoping fate would bring them abundance. They ranged in appearance from clean-cut and tidy, to festering mounds of rotten fabric trimmed with flies, but they were so dense, I had trouble identifying individuals.

I parked at the store, and before I had time to open the truck's door, there was a soft tap on the window. I regarded the face of a less-than-young woman with a determined expression, likely Latina by her appearance. I was also aware that there were several others loitering not far behind her, making an effort to seem disinterested. I sighed and stepped down from the big truck.

"Excuse me, sir. I have a question for you."

She was definitely a native Spanish speaker. I smiled. "Go ahead."

She smiled in return, as if some connection had been forged. I immediately regretted smiling.

"I am looking for work on a farm. I have a tent and everything I need. Do you need help?"

The three men in the background were straining their ears. I tried a sympathetic smile this time. "No, sorry. But good luck!" I turned to leave, but she persisted.

"Possibly you will need some help soon! I have a phone number. Maybe you could take it and call me when you are ready for workers?"

I wanted to flee. A small group from further off had caught sight of the interaction and was moving at speed in my direction. I didn't want to be rude.

"We really don't need the help, but I guess you can give me your number, and if I hear of anything I could let you know... But it's not likely," I added, hoping to reaffirm the situation.

She hastened to write her number and thanked me profusely while trying to insert comments about her skill level as a trimmer. I nodded and turned to go. There was another standing behind me. They all looked the same.

"Excuse me, sir, I was wondering...."

"Not now, sorry, good luck. I have to go, all the best," I blurted as I slipped past and stalked towards the store trying to look unapproachable.

On my way back to the truck, I was apprehended three more times. The final, a graying Slovak, cast his head forcefully downward at my rejection.

"Just tell me one thing. Is there any hope at all? I spent all my money to come here, and I have been sitting for days, just waiting. Is there even a chance?"

"I dunno," I said honestly

Holy shit, that is quite a scene in Garberville and Redway. I've never witnessed crowds like that looking for trim work! I had eight people ask me for work and I had only two stops: store and gas station. And those were just the ones who managed to corral me. I thought they might just dive into the back of the rig as I drove off."

Logan chuckled. "Yeah, kind of wild these days. It's because you were driving the truck. You look like a big Ball Capper. They are a staple now. Everyone is calling them trimmigrants. It's kind of interesting because they really are immigrant workers. They're practically all from Argentina and Chile. I guess those guys caught wind of the scene and figured out it was a good way to make some cash. It's really exploded the last couple of years. Nobody is paying more than a hundred-fifty a pound now, and nobody feeds the trimmers anymore, so a lot of the usual crowd quit because they don't think it's worth it, or they can just work from home. There are a lot of Oregonians who don't have any reason to come down anymore, they just work little gigs at home, and it isn't such an endeavor—no tent, no living outside, no shitting in a hole. But it is still lucrative for a lot of foreign folk, even with the flight. They work hard, trim well, work long hours, leave with a bunch of cash."

"Sounds industrial," I retorted. "They are here for the business. The farmers want that, I suppose."

Logan shrugged. "I mean, yeah, you have to find ways to cut costs now, and trimmers are a huge expense. If you can find someone who will do the work cheaper and just as good, you pretty much have to. It's not an unknown opportunity anymore, Benji. Whole new communities are getting into it. Remember when we were the foreigners? Now there are huge areas owned by the Hmong. They are second, third generation Americans who want to stay in the United States. They aren't sending money home; they see an open industry and nobody can tell them they are wrong to get involved. Nice people too. They're living with their families and their communities, and they are great farmers. Very efficient and very fast processing."

Logan stopped to pick his tooth with a nail—a habit of using the wrong tool for the job was deeply ingrained.

He chuckled again. "The cartels are still out there in the National Forest. You can find the exact same articles we used to read about the busts out in Tipsytom. They must not even type new articles. Just print the same one in every paper. It's the Bulgarians who are a bit scary. They are in this area and you hear about them using some muscle with the locals. Have a bit of a mafia vibe. So... it's a pretty diverse crowd these days. The immigrants are willing to trim the weed that the locals aren't. What are you gonna do?"

As it turned out, there were still plenty of trimmers from the old guard. And trim scenes still happened as they had, at least in regards to their function. They all camped at the property and stayed for a month. They sat around a table talking, just like the old days, but seemed to regard the experience differently.

We had a crew of ten, and only four of them were Argentine. The rest were "experienced trimmers," and those with experience regarded themselves as professionals. They promised speed and quality (a promise that was not always upheld), and they were not shy about demanding their rights or complaining. They openly compared the weed at our farm with that of other farms and threatened to abandon us for other operations if the incentives offered elsewhere were better—more money, food, indoor lodging.

As "professionals," they could market themselves and their skill-set, and use it as a bargaining chip. Everyone understood that the weed needed to look good in order to compete, but it was costly to keep trimmers around. Even if you didn't feed them, they used water, gas, and electricity. Quality trimmers were a valuable tool, but it was just business. An employee and an employer jostling and making moves to find the right deal.

The pro trimmers seemed disinterested in everything that didn't pertain directly to their work. They talked of crews they worked with in the city who brought them in as organized teams with their own manager and dealt with a whole crop, just working nine to five with weekends free. They had all of their own trimming supplies and paid close attention to their productivity. They kept the industry profitable for themselves by learning how to be better than the others around them. They seemed to consider the Argentines their underlings, people of a lower work status.

"At least there are no tweakers at this farm!" Logan reminded them one day when he overheard someone complain about the foreign faction.

And that was a valid concern. The degenerates and the meth addicts had become a notable presence. They were there to trim because money was easy, and the drugs were, too. They were visible and abundant—zombies leaving a wake of revulsion. Methamphetamine had found its way into Humboldt County and the weight of that sad bane hung heavily on the shoulders of the community. Crime rates were high; murder and robbery was a common conversation. Residents were fearful and paranoid. Stories of people robbing their neighbors, and violent gangs coercing residents into selling their property echoed through the hills. People locked their gates and avoided eye contact on the roads. The dark side of the illegal industry was prevalent in southern Humboldt where the perception of easy, untracked money was just too tempting, and people lived in vulnerably remote cabins with only a couple of dogs to look after them.

There was a darkness in that stunning little redwood region, and it made me sad. The dangerous side of an illegal industry had dug its claws into marijuana and reiterated that opportunities for unregulated cash will bring those looking for freedom, *and* bring those looking for freebies.

And when the disease of fear gnaws deeply enough into a community, growth fails and walls are constructed to keep out the foe. As an unfortunate byproduct, they keep out the would-be friends as well.

I knew that in Trinity, and in some of the other ganja strongholds inaccessible to the cities, this presence was not as strong, but to my observations, it was just another factor contributing to the decline of an era.

I was in the grocery store parking lot once again trying to avoid the attention of the hopeful trimmers occupying the edges of the lot, when an aged lady with long frizzled white hair and a bent body returned to her pickup nearby.

"Eggs, yogurt, and kitty-litter. Twenty-six dollars! It's blatant robbery, just eating is going to run me out of business."

It was true, the greed of the grocery stores in Redway and Garberville were legendary. They charged exorbitant prices because people had no other options.

I replied with understanding and the elderly woman realized she had an audience.

"I've been living here and growing pot for forty years, and never have I been worried that I couldn't afford to stay in my own town. You watch, next year us old-timers will be sitting on the street with all the foreigners."

I wondered why I was so prone to expositions.

The woman continued. "We were the ones who made it possible for you young guys to do this in the first place, and now we're just gonna have to pick up and go. Leave our homes where we raised our families. Because everyone wants more more more. Well, I'm done, they finally beat me. I always thought it would be the cops, but in the end, it was my neighbors. The greedy youngsters who just wanted more. And now they have their laws and their legal blah blah blah, and all us old guys are gonna be sittin on the sidewalk looking for trim work. You watch. Seventy percent of us will be out of business next year."

She breathed heavily for a moment, catching her breath, regrouping so that she could say it all.

"When I was young, we all had to rely on one another, we needed one another, and everyone was generous and helpful. Now everyone is thinking about themselves, getting what they can and hoarding it up, not paying people what they deserve, not working as friends. It's all just evil capitalists now. Selfish, stingy, greedy! The time of the people is gone! The time of the money is here! Goodbye!"

She clambered into her rig and drove off in slow anger.

After the work season ended, I drove out to the Tipsytom to visit Jona and Nick. I was pleased to find that little had changed. Well, that's not true. The property had continued to expand and there were numerous new buildings and a great many signs of active living. I saw no indication anyone intended to abandon the Tipsytom.

Both Nick and Jona said that they would grow as long as they could make a profit, but neither of them seemed to care a whole lot. It was, as I had always known—they were there for the life.

"Oh, the valley isn't as active as it was a few years back. A lot of people have moved on," Jona said, "but we have lots of friends who come to visit. I'm ok with that. My community has always been scattered. We get together when we can."

We were sitting by the creek. The late November rains had descended into the valley and the river was already swollen and moving fast. I looked at the ring of hills surrounding the valley— they were immune to the changes happening elsewhere, or at least slower to catch on. That part of the world was isolated, and nobody could easily loiter, no trimmigrants were sitting on the curbs, no city traffic passing through. I realized how miraculous it was that so many people had come to the Tipsytom at all.

When I left the valley, I knew I was satisfied. I had expected a conclusion to the story, but had simply been reminded that there is no such thing. Over the years, the fate of a little culture in the hills always had the potential to take this path or that path or maybe another path. It stands as it is, and from this point onwards, it may continue to do the same: take one path, or another, or maybe another. But what matters the most to me is that it had a moment in time—a moment where the right components came together and created the spark of something different. And the stories, and the experiences, and the lives touched remain indelible for the ages, like little glowing embers waiting for a chance to rekindle.

The cannabis culture has already changed the world, but final outcomes, influences, and what the ultimate impact will be is uncertain. What does this strange and magical plant that quietly affects so many lives still have to offer? Will the changes be industrial, and legal, and social... just in respect to its use? Or will the silent values that it helped nurture spark other, less expected, but more powerful changes?

During the years I observed and participated in the communities of the Northern California and Southern Oregon marijuana farms, I was with a sense of hope and optimism. In spite of the challenges, conflicts, and tragedies, there was a thread of forward movement and a belief in change.

My ardent wish is that the passion for change that grew and was nurtured during that time will find a way to continue expanding through other means, and that the work done will be carried into other communities and other environments by its countless progenitors. They are all still out there, and they have lived a dream. They carry with them the hope of a brighter tomorrow, and hope has a magical way of growing.